What Would Gary Gygax Do?

Writer: Tim Cundle

Artist: Rachel Evans

*The Hallowed Halls of Hardcordia &
Super Justice Punk Rock Trio*

Writer: Tim Cundle

Artist: Jethro Kamba-Wall

Published by Earth Island Books
Pickforde Lodge
Pickforde Lane
Ticehurst
TN5 7BN

wwww.earthisland.co.uk
© Copyright Earth Island Publishing Ltd

First published by Earth Island Publishing 2020

The moral rights of the author have been asserted.

ISBN 978-1-9997581-4-1

Printed and bound in Great Britain by Longridge

Earthisland
publishing

For Emma and Siobhan. Always.

Contents

Foreword

I feel like an imposter writing a foreword for this, Tim Cundle's first collection of short stories. I mean what qualifies one for writing an introduction to a legitimate author's work? I am not a celebrity friend nor an author in my own right. Hell, I've never even met Tim in real life despite us having existed in the shared microcosm of punk rock for the better part of the past thirty years. Nevertheless, when Tim asked me to do this my monumental ego would simply not allow me to pass up on it even though the prevailing rational part of my brain was screaming 'No. No. No' – despite all that here we are....

From my limited understanding of the form, writers have a decision to make when putting these collections together. Are they individual stories standing or falling within their own tiny universes or are they thematically linked tales, sharing common locations, settings or characters? Tim Cundle manages to successfully combine both formulas within this impressive anthology.

Fifty something tales of life, love, death and drugs. An exercise in falling down, growing up and lashing out. The commonality between these tales, the thread that weaves the whole thing together is a bittersweet perspective that suggests that in spite of all the piss and vinegar, Tim isn't quite ready to surrender just yet.

Sure, it's bitter and cynical and there's a tangible stench of black coffee emanating from every page, but the passion that drives the writing is not that of someone who welcomes defeat willingly. Tim survives his own abuse and disappointments with the dogged determination of an ageing prize-fighter. Soaking up the body blows, still waiting for the opportunity to land that big right hand that changes the game. It's an outlook I find myself very familiar with as the rebel yell of defiant youth slowly becomes a scream into the abyss of middle age as life grinds inevitably towards death. As someone who sits within the same cultural demographic as the author it's impossible to read What Would Gary Gygax Do? and not feel an immediate connection with the subject matter.

The McClaren Theory is a salty observation on band life that anyone who has ever trawled around the toilet circuit in a rust bucket van will surely be able to relate to. The eternal battle; on one side creativity, defiance, enthusiasm and anger versus the disappointments, the fist fights, the gigs where three people pay in, the inter-band conflicts that gnaw down to the bone and hollow you out and on and on. But still, in spite of all that disheartening shit, we persist.

There's stuff about growing up as a bored punk in a shitty little town and all the wild schemes and the mischief you create just to kill the time until that chance to get out and get on finally arrives. Then there's *Bargain Basement Rebellion* and its reflections on punk rock ideals versus putting a meal on the table. Convincing yourself you are maintaining your integrity whilst your mates drop the baggage and chase the high powered job, the nice house, the vanilla Instagram feed. The endless spiral of blood pact friendships born in the defiant heat of teenage summers slowly cooling into occasional acquaintance, inevitably becoming that person you used to know, that sometimes 'likes' pictures of your dog on social media.

All this sounds pretty miserable but Tim delivers his ruminations upon the species with enough caustic wit and blood in his teeth to keep What Would Gary Gygax Do? on the right side of naval gazing self-absorption. Each story reads like a caffeine frazzled 'Fuck You' to polite society and it's bullshit expectations whilst tipping a glass to still being out of step with the world.

Nathan Bean

Nathan Bean was born and dragged up in Margate but now lives in exile in Leeds. By day he teaches kids with special educational needs. By night he is a prolific "ex-member of..." numerous punk and metal bands, an occasional pugilist, reluctant podcaster and accidental games designer. A published music writer, and author of death threats, he is currently working on his first collection of short stories.

Acknowledgements

Thank-you: Ma for always being there no matter what, Donna, Harriet and Jonathon, Molly Cook, my partner in "crime" Rachel Evans, David Gamage, Louise Gamage , Everyone at Earth Island Books, Rhodri "Poggles" Dawe, Ian Pickens and Jonathan "Satan" Evans (the Cider Road Trip Gang), Jim Dodge, Martijn Welzen, Chris Andrews (my brother from another mother and podcasting compadre), Tom Chapman, Nathan Bean, Sophie Francois, Tony Fyler, Jason Thomas, Daniel Forst, Mike Wild and Jeff Goddard (the Mass Movement crew), my fellow Lantern Timothy Schwader, Alan Wright — you'll always the best of us brother, Ian Glasper, Mark "Splodge" Lodge, James "Jay X" Connors, All Time Old Time (Gavin, Darrel and Chris) for riding 'Space Mountain' with me, Charlies Family Crisis (Darren, Ian, Pixie, Tony and Sion) for four years of blood, sweat, shows, demo's and tears, Stephen Nanda, Jethro Wall, Heath Crosby, Adam Caradog Thomas, Pete Williams, Michael Davies, Simon Phillips & Cheap Sweaty Fun for twenty years of punk rock mayhem, George Tabb, Mike Beer City, Brady Webb, Joel Meadows and Tripwire, Dean Jeffrey Beddis, Wayne "Pig" Cole, Welly and Artcore, Doug W. Marohn, Kathryn Coleman, Chris Kyle, Anna Hinds, Leanne Toy, Ross O'Brien the hippie dippie Goth King of Nothing and Everything In-between, Alexandros "Alex" Anesiadis, Richard Torres, David "Dog" O'Grady, Marcus "Mivvi" Davis, Beth Dewhurst, Tim "Bunky" Davies, Buff Harris, Richard "Flid" Bryant, John Joseph, Pat Mills, Neil Randle & Bang-On Brewery, Paul "The Gent" Jenkins, Gee Lewis, James "Mangina" Harris, Dayle "Kate" Millward, Steve "Britt" Britain, Tony Maher and Apathy & Exhaustion, Jasper Bark, Jim Mcleod & The Ginger Nuts of Horror, Denise Graham, Ann Jones, Cathy Russo, Mike Prydie and Mark "Warmer" Williams – I'll see you guys on the other side, Al & Flipside, Blaine & The Accused AD, Mousetalgia for keeping the spirit alive, Paul Bearer & Sheer Terror, Bad Religion, Youth of Today, Joe and D.O.A., Slapshot, Underdog, Roger, Vinnie & Agnostic Front, Ratos De Parao, The Bruisers, Circle Jerks, Blood For Blood, Jerry's Kids, Ignite and all the other bands whose music kept me going when all else failed, The Doombuggies Spookshow, Fatman Beyond (Marc Bernardin & Kevin Smith), Marvel Comics, DC Comics, Sarah Mather and all of the other incredible PR's at Titan Books, Dark Horse Comics, 2000AD, Cardiff Devils, WWE, ROH, ISW, ICW, FWA, Stan Lee, Henry Rollins and the one and only, E. Gary Gygax.

Dedicated to the memory of Audrey Harris - You showed me the way, set me on the path and gave me hope in the darkest of moments. I miss you.

"I am a patient boy,
  I wait, I wait, I wait,
"My time is like water down a drain..."
Waiting Room – Fugazi
Lyrics and music by Ian McKaye, Brandan Canty,
Guy Picciotto. Copyright Fugazi/Dischord Records.

"And I'm tired of telling you this tale.
"My brain's fried. And my thoughts
  are in braille.
"I've learned nothing, but what not to do.
"These moments of clarity are precious and few.
"I had a close one (what do you mean?).
"I almost knew 'fun' (what did you see?).
"Too close to the sun (will you survive?).
"Well I'm too dumb to die, too smart
  to stay alive."
Ain't Alright – Sheer Terror
Lyrics by Paul Bearer, Copyright Sheer
Terror/Reaper Records

WHAT WOULD GARY GYGAX DO?

TIM CUNDLE

1

The McClaren Theory

So, there we were, sitting around waiting for the bat phone to ring, hoping to God that we didn't have to play another show for the hippies who had made our lives a living hell throughout ninety-six. Suddenly the silence was shattered by the piercing ring of the glorified tin on a piece of string. You could have heard a pin drop as everyone held their breath, promising all kinds of things if we could just get away with it this one time. The answer came − "Crocker's asking if we can be there in an hour". Fuck.

Right, before I go any further, I'd better explain a few things. Charlies Family Crisis, the band that I used to scream, shout, yell, whatever for, needed a space to rehearse after being kicked out of our last place (a testicle chilling super cooled garage, with no room to piss and a trickle of electricity provided by two moth eaten old leads) for being too loud and not contributing enough money to the Friday and Saturday night fund of the two alcoholics − whose sanity was in severe doubt after months of drinking floor polish − who owned the property. In short, we were up shit creek without a paddle. Following an eternity searching through spaces vacant, we found a place that seemed to be the answer to our prayers. A hippie collective based in Llantrisant owned a shop, and we could use the back room for ten quid a time. At last, somewhere we could make as much noise as possible and not have to answer to anyone. It seemed too good to be true. It was.

Arriving at the shop was like taking a trip into the Twilight Zone. I kept expecting to hear a voice in the background saying: "Imagine if you will five young men...". The only stuff this shop sold was the kind of new age shit you'd expect to find in yuppie heaven. Crystals to help your aura, masks carved by old Mexican women and paintings by artists so obscure that even their own mothers didn't remember them. But figuring that the place was owned by hippies, we assumed that all said items would be fairly priced, after all the owners were products of the Summer of Love which taught all of its disciples that "Bread was like, obsolete, man". Don't believe a fucking word of it. It was the biggest pile of overpriced crap that I'd ever had the misfortune to lay my eyes on. The hippies had joined the nineties and got themselves a real good dose of capitalist fever. It was no longer "Smile on your brother", but "Fuck your brother over for a quick buck". But hey, it was a place to rehearse, so we moved our shit in and started to play. What followed was two and a half years of taking shit, having rehearsals cancelled at the last minute and being expected to drop everything at a moment's notice and do "X" amount of favours for the shrewd business men that the hippies had become.

Worse was to come though. The hippies started organising shows and asking us to play. No problem, we'd play anywhere for anyone as long as they didn't fuck us over. Every show we played for them, they screwed us in one way or another – no promotion (there is nothing as uplifting in this world as turning up to play and finding out that your audience consists of the landlord and your girlfriend), last minute show cancellations (turning up only to find out that nobody knows who you are) and getting stiffed on your travel expenses (scraping the pennies together while some Fagin looking motherfucker pockets your cut of the door). Being the people we are though, we just used to shrug it off and smile as they stuck it to us straight up our collective back passages.

The final straw came in May when we were due to play the Llantrisant free festival organised by...yeah, you can guess. I was going through the sort of heavy duty family problems that soap opera writers can wring six months of storylines out of and time was something that I didn't have to spare. I went to great lengths to explain this to them, and each time they replied with the same old tired bullshit, "You'll go on at the right time, don't worry". Was it too much to ask for? Apparently, it was. Three bands were given our slot, and I lost the only chance I'd ever have to make my peace with one of the most important people in my life. I swore then and there never to do another favour for the gathering of parasites who instantly became my Nemesis.

Anyway, back to the beginning. Somehow we'd been persuaded to play for them again, agreeing in principle simply to keep the peace. I guess it was a case of if we say yes, they'll probably forget about it and there won't be a problem. Only they didn't forget. We received our instructions, and off we went. To get to the place we were playing, which turned out to be an old farmhouse three hundred feet above the Pontycymmer valley, we had to drive up an "old lane" which would lead us to the front door of the venue. Okay. The lane turned out to be an old dirt track no wider than a baby's arm, with the added bonus of there being a sheer drop on both sides which in turn were engulfed in sheer darkness. Wonderful. By some miracle we managed to get to the top and turn our transport around without plunging over the sides and dying in a couple of burning wrecks surrounded by sheep shit. Next step, get to the barn without puking due to the pervading odour of various dead things and overripe excrement. Did that and somehow to managed set up in the barn using a generator that was balanced, along with our jumbled together, budget equipment on a straw covered floor, while praying that someone wouldn't light the whole place up with a carefully discarded cigarette. Thanks to whatever deity was looking down on us we didn't perish in a ghastly hippie inferno and played the show while focusing on the shit encrusted walls instead of downing tools and kicking the shit out of the hippies sprawled around us in different stages of intoxication. We played, we packed up our gear and got the fuck out, swearing that if we ever saw the hippies again bad things involving coffins and gaol time would happen. And I swore to myself that I'd never do another favour for them again. Not ever. I managed to stick to the letter of my oath for less than three weeks. The hippie is a crafty, cunning creature, a lesson that I didn't learn until it was far too late.

Is there a point to all of this? There sure is. No matter what else Malcolm McClaren said or did, he got it dead on balls accurate when he said, "Never trust a hippie", there's only so much goodwill in the world, and only so many favours you should do for people. Don't get taken for granted and don't let people fuck you over. They're going to try, so stand up for yourself and don't take any shit. Be careful out there.

2

What Do You Mean,
I'm Already Dead...

Did your parents ever tell you where they were and what they were doing when John Fitzgerald Kennedy was assassinated and when NASA first landed on the moon? They're the precious moments that people remember for eternity, the split second reactions that are frozen forever; the vulgar immortality that marks the passing of a generation.

What did I get? Star Wars. Ask any forty-something if they remember seeing Star Wars for the first time and the response will always be the same. They'll go misty eyed and tell you every little detail, exactly what the weather was like and how many hours they spent waiting to get into the cinema. Star Wars was the seventies' benchmark that inspired legions of wide eyed, imaginative juveniles to look to the stars and begin to believe in something better. Something different.

It was a cold, wet mid-summer evening, my Dad bought me an ice cream and the screen exploded in an orgy of sound and colour. Strange heroes and leather clad monsters with a fondness for making crank calls to nubile young virgins, heavy breathing and uniforms, played peek-a-boo in a far flung corner of the universe. Another human endeavour wasted on the many and forced on the few, regurgitated time and time again in case we missed the point, too blind to see and stupid to care. It's history in the making young man, turn away for a second and you'll be left behind, a remnant of an uncaring age. Where were you when the children of the disaster epic fled en masse to grab a piece of the pie? I feasted until I could eat no more, for I am a child of seventy-two, filled by greed and bereft of hope. Forever and ever, Amen.

3
Filed, Numbered and Indexed

Some people collect stamps or have an obsessive interest in sports, I play in bands. It's what I do. It's not a fact that I'm particularly proud of, nor is it my main topic of conversation at social gatherings. Just another component in another complex machine, labelled "organic", for want of a better description. I've never viewed music as a "career option", that's something best left to the unwashed exponents of bad heavy metal, media junkies craving toxic overload. That specific department was taken care of, the cards laid on the table, when I was sixteen years old, by a guidance counsellor who had another twenty cases to handle before he could break for lunch.

"I've reviewed your file and decided that you should either work for one of the major corporations in a management role or devote yourself to teaching future generations, moulding them so that they too can become good citizens."

It wasn't exactly what he said, to be honest I wasn't paying that much attention, but the general gist of the conversation was along those lines. In one ear and out the other. Oh well, maybe I'll pay more attention next time. Maybe. While the thought of accumulating vast riches was more than a little appealing, I didn't want to make my fortune by drinking the sweat from the backs of third world countries. As for teaching, it took me enough time to accept responsibility for my own life and its fetid direction and I'd be fucked if I was to become a drill instructor for a new squad of grunts day in, day out for the next thirty years. No, my path lay along a different road. During one of my creative moments, I decided to try "higher" education, earn another qualification that entitled me to enter any profession at the bottom and stay there. I lasted a year before finally giving in to the theory that it was another three years of school – albeit under an alternative name. University is still the only place I've been where adults are treated like children and seem to enjoy it. Higher education? A preparatory institute for idiots, delaying reality as long as humanly possible. Like many before me, I took a variety of shit jobs in order to pay for any subversive activity that happened to be the special of the day. I cleaned up after tourists, catered to geologists' every professional whim and helped drug addicts and alcoholics to continue their chosen life styles as a trusted advisor.

There has only been one constant during my quest to find fulfilling employment. I've always been in a band. Churning out punk rock for the last goodness knows how long many years and for the first time I've taken a break, a vacation, a well earned rest. It isn't time for the collective hand-shake or the gold wristwatch, just some down time to try and put the pieces of my life back together again. Hammer down the lines warped by frustration, making sure they all fit before moving on to plan B.

I've been through more bands than Imelda Marcos had shoe salesmen. Some lasted a couple of weeks and one four years. The basic rules never change though, don't alter one bit. The first step is easy, putting the band together. Sift through the scumbags, losers and wasters for long enough and eventually you'll find a stable line up. How long it's going to last is another matter. If you assume that nobody likes each other and that it's going to be a constant battle of egos and personalities then everything should, according to the collective laws of the punk rock guidebook, be okay. Besides, a fist fight at intermittent intervals never does any harm.

Music? Once again assume that your "stable" line up is going to fight over the construction of each song. A vocalist will insist that the lyrics must be at the forefront so that the audience can understand his unique vision, while a drummer only wants everything to reach a crescendo that will shatter a normal ear drum at fifty paces.

Guitarists? They're happy enough to masturbate

over a varied ensemble of effects and are best left alone trying to adapt phase variants and other mind boggling shit to the most basic of three chord structures. After you've written and finalised a set list, which will bear no resemblance to the original ideas projected by each individual member, it's time to take your music to the people, who in turn will reward you with praise and promises of devotion. I've said it before, and am doubtless fated to say it again, reality and fantasy are two sides of the same coin. They're not destined to meet and dreams are wishful thinking amplified by crippled logic. Show after show after show, you eventually realise that what started as a mistake has become a prison sentence, locked down with a world of wonder waiting on the other side.

Occasionally, realisation will set in sooner rather than later. Rarity is a blessing earned through attendance at the school of hard knocks and not something handed to the poor fools who just happen to have been waiting in line since the doors opened. Nothing lasts forever and all good things must come to an end. Social behaviour isn't one of humanity's strongest suits and Sartre was right, hatred is a direct product of spending too much time with other people. Why do I still do it? Because it's cheaper than therapy and I've got an idealistic streak a mile wide. Some of us were made to suffer.

4

Between The Third Rock
And A Hard Place

Let's get one thing straight right from the start, the universe wasn't created in six days and no one died for my sins. There's no pearly gates, no white bearded old guy waiting for you on the other side and no celestial garden to trip through, rejoicing in the afterlife for all eternity. This is it and you'd better enjoy it while you can because there are no second chances. It's all a lie; we've been played for suckers since the dawn of time, jumping on the salvation bandwagon, singing along with the heavenly karaoke, too scared to face the truth. Shut your eyes, put your wallet and faith in the hands of a preacher with a hotline to Jehovah and everything will be hunky dory. A place on the stair lift to the stars guaranteed. Bullshit. When was the last time that the Pope paid your rent? Wake up and smell the coffee.

Faith turned to blind devotion and in the process made a monkey out of each and every one of us. My ancestors swung in the trees and ate bananas, they didn't spring fully formed from the dust ready to fornicate for the greater glory of the Lord. The only forbidden fruit in the garden of Eden was man's ability to question all that he was told. Evolution is a proven fact and the world is littered with its evidence. But a higher power guiding us through daily life? Show me a miracle and I'll be the first in line. Until someone can, I'll put my faith in humanity being the master of its own destiny. I'll take science over religion every time, the scales tipping in the favour of the laws of physics and chemistry rather than half-baked myths and legends about a carpenter's son and his followers.

Religion has been and always will be the root of all evil. If I believe in evil, then I've got to accept the force of good, right? So be it, doesn't mean that I have to accept divinity. Good and evil are flip sides of the same coin and lie at the very heart of man's nature. For every action, there is an equal, opposite reaction, a way to maintain the equilibrium that is fundamental to the existence of our planet. The notion that these forces can be separated is not only foolish but dangerous. Heaven and hell? They're the same fucking place separated merely by spaces between stops on an endless wheel that's been turning since the dawn of the universe.

The branches of the tree of religion have spread out and become thicker, encompassing the globe, tightening its grip in the aftermath of the millennium with no refuge or respite; there's a church for each and every man and woman on Earth and if you don't like the one you're offered, wait around for a while and another one is bound to pass by. Only the weak need a leader, need to gather under the shadow of an omnipresent deity who rewards the faithful at a time of his choosing. Persecute minorities and place the blame elsewhere, it can't be the fault of the church. Blame the Jews for the fact that you're poor, they control the world economy because the Catholic Church certainly doesn't believe in splendour or taking the food from its congregation's mouths in order to maintain the Vatican, does it?

Blessed are the meek for they shall inherit the world. Crock of shit. Look at the world you're living in. Run by corporations who thrive on competition and the principle that it's every man for himself, you've got to get tough to have any chance of survival. The only thing the meek stand to inherit is a size nine in the teeth as they're trampled over and left for dead. Stay quiet, hand over your money and don't question a thing you're told. Treat women as second-class citizens who can't make decisions for themselves – don't they know abortion is murder? What about the doctors and women murdered by the righteous for daring to believe in the freedom of choice. Victimisation by zealots, and the motherfuckers who built the temples that could be used as shelters for the homeless, is nothing new. Remember the

Salem witch trials, the attempted destruction of the Jewish race by the Nazis? All of which can be firmly placed at the door of religion, as it continues to develop its taste for war, a genocidal junkie craving its fix as humanity grows; the master that kills its slaves in an effort to prove that it's the only one fit to spread the word of the supreme entity.

A supreme entity? No such thing. The unshakeable belief in a higher power is another example of humanity's immaturity, a race that's been trying to avoid growing up and facing the consequences of its actions. We installed a father figure, an overseer, someone who would punish us when we were naughty and reward us when we were good. It's about time that we packed our bags and kissed dad goodbye and set off on our own path to find our destiny. Find out what's really waiting for us as we pool our resources and work together for the first time since history began. We'll either fail or succeed; it's as simple as that. And if we do fail, at least nobody can say we didn't give it our best shot, and that we finally paid attention to the voice of reason that's been crying out since the Big Bang. Maybe we should just shut up and listen for a change instead of always trying to be the loudest kid in the room. After all, no one likes a bully.

5

Bargain Basement Rebellion

Punk rock and hardcore were always supposed to be the last bastions of the underground, a refuge for misfits, fuck ups and those tired of living by the rules determined by a system founded on corruption, hypocrisy and greed. It provided a voice for the directionless, refused to bow to the rules of the capitalism and proudly displayed a middle finger to the established music industry. Nobody would do it for us, so we'd do it ourselves, and be damn proud of what we'd fashioned, knowing that we'd bucked the system and there was nothing that they – an elusive they – could do about it. Perfect. When your brother or sister fell, you picked them back up, dusted them down, and showed them that they could get back on their feet again, that they were somebody and not the insignificant number or name they'd been told they were since day one. Speak out or forever hold thy peace. Don't let the bastards grind you down, stand up and prove your worth. A network of dissidents fuelled by the depression of everyday life, struggling against the negativity forced on them by their elected members of state.

A scene is only as strong as the people who comprise it, but strength came from unity through individuality, striving for a common set of purposes and goals. Everyone in the scene remembers first discovering punk and hardcore, the energy and excitement that flowed from the speakers and filled them with a sense of urgency that dissipated their lethargy and removed their overpowering loneliness and isolation. Testing marksmanship, target up, crosshairs in place, fire when ready. Me? After my first exposure to it, I had to hear more and before I knew it, I was drawn into a place warmer than any I had ever known. I wasn't crazy, and all things weren't as they seemed. Life would never be the same, I'd sold my soul for punk rock, made my deal with the devil and I'd never been happier. There were no set rules, it meant something different to everyone, and that was its beauty. No laws, just guidelines, you could make it up as you went along and to hell with the consequences. Ideas and originality pulled together, creating a weird geometry inside which we all resided, urged on knowing that each played a valid part, and if we disagreed, fuck it, everyone is entitled to their point of view. Like so many movements before, the extremists saw us and decided they could use us in order to achieve their objectives. Unlike previous movements though, punk and hardcore thrived on individuality and could smell evil, we'd been touched by the hand of slavery before, and recognised it when faced with it again, albeit in a different package. Some fell for the lies and deceit, but for every one we lost one more came along, confused, alone, seeking rebirth.

Nothing could have prepared me for the first time I went to a punk show. Sure I'd been to metal shows before, organised around a militaristic time scale, enough equipment to start a world war, and the hero worship that separated bands from their hordes of fans who'd come to see them. Punk was minimalist in the extreme, bands jumping up and doing it, there were no boundaries, everyone was there to have a good time. There was none of that insipid "I'm cooler than you" metal grandstanding and no one gave a shit what costume you turned up in. It didn't matter how you looked, it was a state of mind. But it came at a price. The "normal" folks thought it was all sorts of fun to subject punk rock kids to the odd physical and verbal beating. They didn't matter, though and just made me stronger and reinforced my belief in myself. Fuck 'em if they thought they could break me. Sticks and stones, water off a duck's back. I willingly paid the cost with my blood, sweat and tears. I was helping to build for the future; opening people's eyes and making them question the things that had once seemed absolute.

Evolution is part of the natural order, change is necessary for things to grow and flourish. If they don't, they soon become forgotten, leaving only bones and ruins for historians to examine and discuss, left on show for passing tourists in the hallway of existence. Movement can always be measured, and punk rock came on in leaps and bounds, becoming faster, harder and more relevant with the passage of time. From the scene's little acorn the big oaks grew, and punk developed branches, movements within movements. Pop punk, hardcore, crust core, peace punk, grind core, speed core, metal core, anarcho punk, you name it, we'd love it, desperately trying to separate one band from another. As each branch moved further from the body, so the whole thing became weakened and structurally unsound. Still we looked to the future with hope, knowing our roots had been firmly planted, watered and with loving care allowed to grow and blossom. In the background they (remember the ever elusive they?) had been plotting, planning, waiting to move in when the time was right. They had tried to reassure the world that punk was dead, and when it hadn't worked, had slunk away and licked its wounds, retreating so they could return to fight another day. To say that punk was unprepared for the monster it was to face would be an understatement. It didn't have a fucking clue. The wind direction had changed and money became the byword on everybody's lips. Change had come, and

I remember seeing the apparition, the ghost of Christmas Future, parked outside a club, the band inside sound checking before they played their set that night. Instead of the usual collection of beat up vans that had seen better days, it stood there, blocking out the sun and shrouding the club in a glove of darkness; a tour bus. It was a gleaming, metal beast that stood two stories tall and sixty foot long. I touched its cold skin and knew that the future was fucked.

Companies started throwing money at punk, and eager to taste something new, it bit the forbidden fruit, relishing the taste of its rotten flesh. We were wide open and defenceless, the fangs sunk in, sucking the lifeblood from our twitching corpse. Don't get me wrong, I'm a firm believer in the theory that says if you can make some money by doing something you love it beats the shit out of working a crappy nine to five. However, there is a world of difference between happiness and over bloated greed. The thing that punk had set out to fight against had consumed it and started to use it as another sellable commodity. If a band makes music and sells that music, then you could say that it's already sold out, a childish romantic notion. Success doesn't hurt the scene. On the contrary it should only benefit it. After struggling for years, being rewarding for working hard is positive reinforcement. Put something in, you're entitled to take something out.

The problem lies in exploitation. Jealously prompts a man to want what another has, and so bands started jumping on the wagon to glory. With no understanding of the movement they proclaimed themselves to be 'hardercore than thou' assumed the "attitudes", the "uniform" and sold themselves to the record companies and public alike, hoping for a fast ride to riches and fame. Bands who had been around before the panic hit, felt the pinch as they watched metal bands strip the scene for every penny they could, and retreated further underground choking back their tears as the scene collapsed. MTV played the tapes of the acceptable face of rebellion and encouraged kids to dye their hair green in order to avoid becoming the establishment. All they did was stretch the establishment's boundaries until rebellion became the social norm. Veterans of bands who had split years before, reformed, chasing the carrot in front of their noses and cash rewards from playing to vacuous kids who longed for a taste of yesterday. Anarchy was replaced by dollar signs as business executives lectured the kids on what was and what wasn't punk. How can you be a punk if you're not wearing the latest two hundred pound shoes and fifty pound tee-shirts? Long time trusted stalwarts grew to like the taste of money and threw their principles away in order to earn a little more and claim their piece of pie. Journalists who had previously loathed everything punk stood for, got inexpensive tattoos and painted themselves as Gurus of hardcore in order to salvage popularity. Brother turned against brother and sister fought sister as all-out war was declared and the scene ripped itself apart. And as everything that I loved slowly began to die, I hid my head in the sand, and hoped that if I ignored it for long enough, it would all go away and everything would somehow revert to the way it had once been. It didn't and now I'm a part of something that I don't even recognise, running to try and stay still on a punk rock Sisyphean wheel. Hell is what you make it and we all forge the bars of our own prisons.

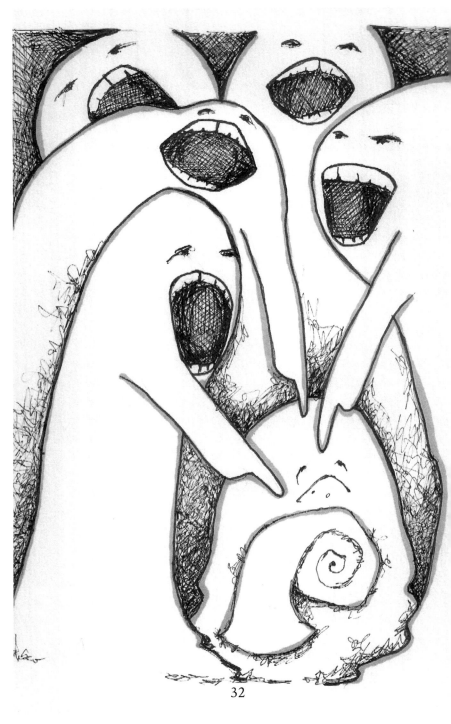

6

Branded, Bought And Sold

They're all the same, the same white walls and grey buildings, and they've all got a special offenders' wing. Some call it the losers club, some geeks corner, call it what you will; it amounts to the same thing. A space the non-entities can call home. Membership was, is, and always will be, non-exclusive, although there are certain rules that the potential applicant should adhere to. Bad haircuts, clothes that don't quite fit or are horribly dated, strange personal habits, hygiene deficiencies and involvement with anything other than sport, all qualify you for a place in the selective grouping that exists on the edge of social functions. I was head hunted before my induction having both a haircut that went out of vogue ten years previously and a preference for music rather than athletics. I'd wanted to play the trumpet and ended up being stuck with the French horn, an instrument usually associated with chess protégés and physics graduates. If you played a brass instrument you were fair game for the idiots whose muscles were bigger than their capacity for learning. Every Monday, hunting season started and there would be at least one kill each week. Being a little smarter than the slow learners meant that we soon found the only escape routes. You either waited for an hour, locked in the music room and missed all of your favourite shows or you ran like the wind, stopping for nothing.

"Thomas is making a break for it, go man, run, don't stop. Oh no, his glasses have slipped and he's slowed down to try and fix them. You can make it, get going. Run, for the love of God, run. Too late, the savages have caught him. I can't watch, it's too brutal".

Running was out of the question, brass instruments are just too fucking big. You'd be lucky to get up to more than a trot carrying the half hundred weight anchor that dragged you down and kept you in check. Fleeing always ended the same way, caught before you even got through the school gates. That's why I wanted to play the trumpet, at least your legs could move while you clutched it to your chest. But the cumbersome tool I'd been burdened with? I began to imagine myself driving a steam roller over the loathsome instrument of my weekly doom as I sat locked in the music room for the fortieth Monday in succession.

The years passed, my haircut changed and I gave up music, cutting the chord that bound me to the rites of subjective torture. To this day, I hate the fucking French horn, just seeing or hearing one will send me into a fit of rage that makes me lash out and push the nearest small child off his or her bicycle. It didn't matter how hard you tried to change the system, it was like the Mafia, once you're in, you're in for life and whether you were sporting glue spikes or a basin cut, if you'd made your mark on the dotted line, that was that. I served my time and waited for that faint glimmer of hope that spelt release, and eventually, as these things always do, it materialised. The sixth form party. You didn't need to be invited, as long as you bought a ticket you could attend. It was open to one and all. We gathered, nerds and geeks alike, drew our plans and dreamed of what been previously been denied to us. Soon everyone would know we were their equals, worthy of their time and conversation.

We met to drink pick me ups, a little Dutch courage, before the party and true to form, a few of the dweeb infantry spilled their guts as nerves and alcohol kicked in. By the time we arrived, the party had been cancelled because of a double booking with a police celebration. Judging wisely, the club owner had decided to give the forces of law and order priority and turned away the droves of school kids who had ventured out, hellbent on making it a night to remember. It was a simple choice, go home and wallow in isolation for another year or follow the herd to the next adventure. You don't need to be a Nobel laureate to figure out which path I and the rest of my fellow outcasts took. The destination was a low rent drinking hole, popularised by the athletic stars of the local schools and entry was usually forbidden to those who didn't conform to the narrow parameters of what was "cool". This time however, the rulebook had been tossed aside and the door flung open to anyone who wished to venture inside. One of our more foolhardy brethren decided that to fully integrate ourselves with the golden community we would need to sample their chosen beverage, and approached a human mountain to ask what this might be.

"What does everyone drink around here?"

"Green or Red Death."

"Really?"

"Yeah, just go up to the bar and ask for one, they'll know what you're talking about."

"Thank you very much."

That was a nice thing to do wasn't it? Not even a hint of malice. Don't be stupid. They'd seen us coming and decided to have some fun with the geeks. Green and Red Death were cocktails designed to celebrate great sporting victories and tasted similar to paint stripper, but the funny thing was, that once you'd had one, you sort of became used to it, and for some strange reason, had to have another. And another, and another, and another, until you couldn't see, stand, speak or remember what your name was. So, we drank and drank until we could drink no more. Laughter turned to concern, which was replaced by euphoria as the locals watched us consume cocktail after cocktail. For one night we couldn't put a foot wrong and we were accepted as human beings, the pallid little playthings of Neanderthals, but human beings nonetheless. They even bundled us into taxis and sent us on our way when, after passing out in pools of our own vomit, our amusement value had worn off.

The acceptance we had craved was ours, and for one night only we rejoiced in our celebrity. We milked it for all it was worth; talking to the women who would usually turn around if they saw us coming and sharing jokes with the muscle-bound barbarians who delighted in making our lives a living nightmare. But when the sun rose the following day, the old social order returned and once again we became the losers' club, destined to sit alone and fantasise about the drunken orgies that might have been. The grass is always greener on the other side and there's nothing worse than being given a taste of what you crave and then having it snatched from your eager grasp. I didn't choose the geek life, the geek life chose me.

7

Watching The World Burn

Ever had one of those nights when you just want to sit back and watch the wheels of industry turn around you? Hang out and do nothing apart from getting so drunk that you've got to move each leg independently, happy to collapse and pass out where you fall, sleeping off a hangover in the nearest flower bed? I've had more than my fair share, but one in particular always springs to mind. I was at a loose end, which was a surprisingly common occurrence, after a ridiculously named band whose entire existence was predicated on shock value rather than talent, the Grave Robbing Virgins or something equally as banal, had cancelled due to unforeseen circumstances. Which usually meant that one of the band members had overdosed and needed a couple of days off to get back on his feet. The bands were almost always men, probably because they craved hero worship and the chance to be idolised by an audience made up of, mostly, pubescent boys who were just as sexually confused as their musical deities. Women had soon learnt that it was far easier to get to the top if they just played and avoided all the degrading shit that went hand in hand with metal – a word that begs to be screamed, legs spread wide apart making the sign of the evil eye with both hands. No, they'd pulled out and left me and my friend Jason to face one of the greatest teenage dilemmas. What to do. We counted our money and decided that our best option was to buy as much alcohol as we possibly could and drink the bloody lot. Imagination was something that we sorely lacked.

The nearly insurmountable hurdle that confronted us was finding a place that would sell copious amounts of fire water to two obviously under age males. I'd always had a hard time trying to buy booze, no matter what I did. Let the bum fluff grow a couple of days, smother myself in aftershave, adopt my deepest voice or assume an air of nonchalance, it didn't matter what glorious subterfuge I attempted, I always failed miserably. It began to affect my confidence, and I started to think that all the store owners licensed to sell alcohol met every month and handed around pictures of the foolhardy youths they'd turned away at the end of their secretive guild's clandestine meetings. Jason knew my problem, but he always sent me in first because the pathetic charade never failed to amuse him. It was the same every single time. I'd get as far as the counter and start to sweat, not the slightly warm, gently perspiring variety, but the kind of sweat that covers your body when you're desperately trying to convince an over-eager policeman that there really isn't any cocaine hidden in any of your pockets. The lady behind the counter would examine me carefully from head to toe, roll her eyes and play along.

"You got any identification?"

Bugger. Never mind, try the old favourite, you never know.

"I appear to have left it at home."

My falsetto tone would have shamed even the most effeminate drag artist.

"In that case, I'm sorry, I can't serve you."

Not having anything better to do I let the scenario play out and left the store empty handed, passing the money to Jason who was, as usual, killing himself with laughter, at my misfortune and expense. Jason had never been turned away and had never failed in the great teenage booze quest. I guess you've either got it or you haven't. I didn't, and he did. I'm certain that he kept whatever it was hidden in a sack under his bed.

"What do you want then?"

I thought about the multi-coloured bottles and the labels that displayed their intoxicating powers.

"Doesn't matter. Booze and lots of it!"

The specifics of taste are lost on the underage drinker. As long as it contains alcohol, it'll do the job. Ask no questions and be told no lies being the most important, and only, rule of teenage drinking.

Five minutes was all it took to accomplish the fearsome task, in and out, no hesitation and no delays. We had our booze and nothing could stop us. Paying no attention to what was in the bottles, we drained them in record breaking time, stopping only to piss as the mood took us. As we drank, we discussed the greatest philosophical questions that had ever been posed, the mysteries of intelligence and whether or not we were alone in the universe. Oh, and we talked about women as well – a subject that formed the backbone of all drunken conversations. The meaning of life was solved and forgotten as we moved on to whether women should shave or wax, which back in those days was a perennial male problem.

All good things have to end, and as the sun started to rise and the bottles lay empty, we began our long journey home. Somewhere, somehow, I broke my nose and managed to scrape half the skin off my face, leaving it a tattered mess and a testament to my woeful drinking ability. For weeks I was plagued by questions about my horrific injuries and rather than admit the truth, my fragile male pride always provided the same answer.

"Me and Jase got jumped by ten blokes and this happened before we could fight them off.'

What was I expected to say? I fell over while drunk? That was the kind of thing that happened to old men who bought dirty magazines and pissed themselves on public transport, not desperate young punks who thrived on attention. Get a fucking life. I was having too much fun revelling in the sympathy bestowed upon me by every girl I bumped into and my newly acquired status as a "hard arse" which was handed down to me by the blokes who listened, fascinated by my tale of false conflict which grew in magnitude with successive rendition. And Jason? Well, he played along, after all he'd come away without a scratch, a badge of honour that propelled him headlong into the same sort of zone of alpha male territory reserved for the likes of Jean Claude Van Damme and Chuck Norris. Is there a moral, or lesson to be learned, from this tale of pathetic debauchery? There sure is. Drinking doesn't always end in misery. Sometimes it can be fun, but every bottle has a bottom and each day a new dawn. It all depends on how you look at things. Is your glass half full or is it half empty? Never let the truth get in the way of a good story.

8

Farewell To The King

I don't make friends easily. Oh sure, I'll talk to people and enter into all the social etiquette bull-shit, nodding politely, pretending to listen intently, all the while letting my mind drift. Did I leave the tap running? Did I lock the back door?

Can't help it, it's just one of those things. I've got enough problems of my own without someone else's weighing me down and I always used to think that I was cynical and didn't trust anyone. Recently though, it was pointed out to me that maybe, and hey this is just a theory, I trusted too easily and when people let me down it hurt like a motherfucker every time. Burned, hung out to dry and taken to the cleaners every single time. Cynicism or faith? They stand between the black and white, blurring into grey, making it difficult to tell one from the other. You pay your money and you take your chance. Ladies and gentlemen, place your bets please, the wheel of fortune is spinning again. Sorry sir, you lost again, but don't worry, there's always next time.

Acquaintances come and go, walking into your life one day, strolling away the next and each time one hitches a ride to Nowheresville, he or she takes a little piece of you with them. It can get to the point where you feel like you've fed the five thousand and there's barely enough left for you to sit down and eat. Please sir, can I have some more? Mentally starving, exhausting and time consuming, friendships demand their pound of flesh and you've got to pay the toll. No one rides for free.

Nobody realises what they have until it's taken away. I'm sure someone famous said that, but who gives a shit? It's just another anecdote from another dead philosopher. You hit rock bottom, there's no way up and it's only the shit that keeps you afloat. Barely. It's at times like this that people seem to flock to you like flies to rotten excrement.

Occasionally though, someone will kick your backside back to the land of the living. Carl was like this. Remove those shit coloured spectacles and walk with me grasshopper. Learn all there is to be learned, exploit it and turn it around until freedom beckons you with open arms. It'll be a long, hard road and you may get tired along the way, don't fly too close to the sun and you'll eventually reach wherever the hell it is you're going and the good life. On your feet soldier, you're fit for a few miles yet. He could face any situation and make you feel like everything was going to be fine while the walls crashed down around you. He made me laugh while the grip of adversity slowly squeezed the eyes from my sockets and made me see the magnifying glass that was held above the mindless insects rushing from one job to the next in the daily grind. If you looked closely, you could see how ridiculous it really was. If you want to end up like that, fine. Before you do though, consider your options. Carefully. Reach for the stars and all things can be yours, be all things to all men, but never be a martyr. Otherwise, a suit and tie would be a fine epitaph to a fine apprentice who had been cast adrift on the sea of madness, searching for an island with Friday and two point four coconuts.

They were some of the best times I ever had, and I was naive to think they'd never end; tripping the light fantastic in top hat and tails, a double act that could have supported Elvis in Vegas on an indefinite run. My quest for the Holy Grail had begun in good company and I could slay dragons and charm princesses. It wasn't to be. Carl fell in battle, another casualty of war, struggling with private demons, a victim of weakness in the fight against drugs. I was left to wander the wasteland, a knight without a cause, the bitter irony of billboard campaigns designed to save the youth of tomorrow from the poisons of today weighing heavily on my heart.

Years passed before I finally used what I'd learnt. Don't grieve for fallen angels. If there is a heaven, I know he's there, drinking the finest wines, partying with goddesses and pissing himself with laughter at mankind's ineptitude. Seize every moment as it comes, walk that tightrope without fear and light a candle for another dead philosopher. Life's too short to be a victim.

9

Later Days And Age Old Lays

In a perfect world, friendships would last forever. Those special bonds formed by time and circumstance would overcome all odds, allowing the moments that you spent together to remain as vital and important as they were on the first time you met. Forget the casual acquaintances that were never meant to last, like the kid who asks you a million questions and wants even more answers after a show, or the girl who hung around for three weeks one summer before the wind changed and sent you in opposite directions. Friends are the people you grew up with and spent those evenings that stretched into forever talking about nothing in particular with; who left their mark on your soul. But it's not a perfect world. So those friendships bloom like a flower, display their radiance, then decay, drying out in the warm air of a humid afternoon, before crumbling to dust and vanishing, leaving only stale memories.

When you're young, you think those days are going to last an eternity, an endless season dragging out in front of you, and have no idea how precious a commodity friendship is. The trips to the zoo when you try to find an animal that's even stranger than the one your friend has picked out, the days spent at the beach building forts from the assorted detritus lying on the shoreline or the times when you did nothing much, but had a blast anyway. Fate steps in and gives you a harsh prod in the ribs, illustrating a few of the ground rules. Better employment prospects and divorce cause families to move and all the well meant promises of written communication are forgotten as soon as the cartoons come on. Education decrees that you should belong to a certain social group, impressing your new friends by bullying the old, while strung out on a guilt trip that lasts a life-time. Whatever the outcome, the final curtain always gets lowered and the most you can manage as it falls is a vague nod to the people whose names have already slipped away.

As with all things, your new friends open new doors for you to explore, infant memories cloud over, the cobwebs gather and they're boxed, stored and sealed away in that dark corner of your mind where everything festers and remains unused and neglected. Being cool becomes the new religion and anything that can harm it is avoided while varying degrees of lethargy separate you from the person you used to be. I remember being told that my school years would be the best time of my life – the same thing was also said to me when I went to university, a quote that's torn directly from page fifty-seven of the parental advice manual. They're lies, blatant untruths and every adult knows they are, but they tell them anyway, because that's just what you do. Life is hard enough for a teenager, dealing with rampant hormones, awkward attempts at seducing the opposite sex (or the same one, depending on the advancement of individual maturity), making sure you're not seen with the "wrong crowd" and somehow trying to blend into the background, without having to wear a perpetual fucking smile. Grin and bear it? Fuck no.

What's to come is even worse. Worse? How can anything be worse than the hell on earth that the developing years thrust upon you? Somehow you manage to survive with just a handful of friends and the pressing issues of partying, drinking and fucking destroy any ideas of independence that might have arisen. The local hangouts become the clubs, bars and pubs that you feel comfortable in as you settle for inebriation and fantasy over drudgery. Friendship gives you a convenient hiding place, a respite from life. If you can't exaggerate about your conquests and drinking ability with your mates, who can you feel good, and lie, about yourself with? The only time you visit the school yard is when you need somewhere to crack open a six pack, a venue in which to talk about how great it was in the old days as you don the gown of all-knowing philosopher at age nineteen. These are the guys you swear allegiance to; there won't be a single thing that will come between you. This is the way it's always going to be and it doesn't get much better than this does it? Let the good times roll.

Of course, bullshit pacts between old friends never last. It's beer talk, a way of filling time as dusk approaches heralding the witching hour and a last gasp attempt to hold on to something that's already slipping away. It's nobody's fault, your priorities change as the world turns and passes you by. The question of money and its privileges becomes one of paramount importance, selling out to gain the credibility and respect that accompany a wallet filled with portraits of dead people and a new sports car. Pucker up and get ready to kiss whatever posterior you need to in order to get ahead, climb to the top of the tree and crack the whip whenever the urge and your new career dictate that you must. There's no time left for the trivial issues, for hanging out and enjoying yourself with the potential competition. Wave them farewell until there's only a couple of you left, toasting the glory of the old days at age twenty-two. Relationships raise their ugly heads and suddenly you'd rather spend your time with your girl or your boy than drinking with your buddies. They're your friends, but which one of them is going to fulfil those needs that creep in when the moon rises. Rationalisation is the first step on the road of impending adulthood and before you know it, you're grown up, ready to start a family and send your kids out to repeat the process all over. It's just the way it is. C'est la vie!

10

Surviving Suburbia

History is one of the most valuable commodities the human race has ever held in its grasp. As a people, we place our faith in the knowledge that we learn from our past mistakes in order to prevent them being repeated, and as individuals we find comfort in memory, knowing that it has shaped the person each of us has grown to become. To understand is to know, and for any man to truly know another he must look to the past. Where did the road split? Why did they turn left instead of right? Attitudes and opinions develop, moulded by the surroundings in which we're raised, our surroundings playing a greater role than any of us would dare dream. Sociologists never forget the most basic of lessons. Home is where the heart is, where the organ that drives every single one of us through daily life lives. It's all a question of nurture versus nature, the age old tired retreat of less able intellectuals.

I grew up like so many others, in small town suburbia, in an area dependent on tourism to sustain it. It's a nice place to visit, but would you really want to live there? Only if you like fun, fun, fun. From day one I was ostracised for too many reasons, each a triviality, unworthy of discussion.

I wasn't the first, won't be the last. As one prisoner broke free, so another started a custodial sentence. School blurred into an endless succession of beatings that didn't abate until my spirit fled and had scattered to the four winds. With each beating I became stronger, and the stronger I became, the longer the assaults lasted. Mother Nature would have you believe that the strong always prey on the weak and if that is the case, what elevates man above the animals? Eventually the lights switched on, I couldn't be broken, the pleasure of my tormentors dissipated as this sordid realisation dawned. Minimal achievement for maximum outlay isn't economically viable, and Business 101 and all of its sordid rules was a favourite of the eighties' child.

Outcasts, one and all, band together out of desperation, reverting to herd behaviour, forced into groups by circumstance. Hopelessness kept me alive and let me rejoice in isolation. Each teenage suicide made me realise that there but for the grace of God go I. A sucker for punishment, I never did things the easy way and one of my only joys was holding on – which pissed my persecutors off far more than rolling over and playing dead. It was a war of attrition and I wasn't going anywhere.

Distance became a choice, they could shove everything up their sanctimonious arses and bleat about whatever tweaked their little motors, it all fell on deaf ears. Sacrifices had to be made and while they fucked each other, watching the planets spin around their little circles, I cast my eyes to the horizon, my emotional baggage fully loaded. It was aboard my imaginary good ship that I first heard the sirens sing. In every small town the best things are hidden below the surface and if you don't pay attention, they'll sail right by. Shining like a beacon in the night was the private Catholic school, a haven for the offspring of the old boy network. My childhood had been filled with stories of how Catholics consorted with Satan and would burn in hell for all eternity, spreading their filth and wickedness. This oppor-tunity was too good to pass up. If you've ever heard the rumours about Catholic girls, let me reassure you, they don't even scratch the surface. There on my doorstep were females, eager to experience everything forbidden by the very nature of their institution. They didn't want money, chiselled features, social graces or silver spoons. They wanted the rejected, the refuse, the misplaced. I found my home. All freaks were wel-comed into their fold and every nasty desire catered for and too.

The tables had turned, flipped upside down and my label changed overnight. I walked what the pretty boys talked. Chinese whispers multiplied my adventures, and who was I to spoil the fun of the elite? Pretty boys were left masturbating to farfetched tales of lust, while their pretty girls invited me in to steal what was theirs by right. Panic set in. They had learned that Utopia would never be opened to them as it was to me. I was the path. I was the way. Blind devotion had convinced them that if it was going to happen to anyone, it had to be them. Boys, Calvinism is a dead religion and capitalism an outmoded concept. The ball was in my court. Their disbelief became a virus that polluted and poisoned their souls. I hope it hurt motherfuckers. What one sees all see and jealousy is a powerful weapon. Something had to be done about the upstart and fast.

Never take your opponents for granted. Always assume the next guy is a lot smarter than you are and tread extremely carefully. Summoned to the hidden chambers of the self-appointed guardians of morality, or teachers as they're commonly known, my chastisement awaited. After all I wasn't one of their protégés.

"We've got a square peg trying to squeeze into one of our nice round holes. The process for dealing with such impudence is clearly laid down. Do I have permission to carry on?"

"Permission granted. Do a thorough job. No mistakes this time."

"Understood."

The inquisition began and I sought to regain

control of the situation by any means possible. As far as I could tell, all avenues were open.

"I think you know why you're here."

"No sir I have no idea."

The first salvo, the big guns had been dragged out far out too early. I had to duck before the shit hit the fan.

"Come now boy, do you think we're stupid?"

Is that a rhetorical question? I hope so, because not a single one of you fuckers is going to like the answer if it isn't.

"No sir, I don't think you're stupid."

Liar. I was sure that I was still a real boy and as there were no strings on me, I assumed my nose hadn't betrayed me. So, I did what came naturally. I acted dumb.

"What exactly do you get up to in your spare time? And by that, I mean the time you don't spend in school?"

Surely this was a violation of my civil rights? What fucking business of theirs was it? I wasn't their responsibility, and had no responsibility to them. My blood started to boil.

"Why do you want to know?"

Wait for it. This should be interesting.

"It has come to our attention that your behaviour outside of school leaves a lot to be desired, and discredits not only yourself but the school as well."

Well, excuse motherfucking me, I thought this country was supposed to be a democracy. I stand corrected.

"What do you mean by that, sir?"

A shape moved in the corner. Number two stood, straightened his jacket and peered through his glasses, the left arm of which was held on by Sellotape. His hair was combed over in a futile attempt to hide his bald head. For a brief moment, I imagined him leaping from the window screaming "I'm bald and I'm free". But as there was about as much chance of that happening as there was of the Pope admitting to a packed Sunday congregation that he whacked off to naked pictures of Dolly Parton, I dismissed the fantasy almost as quickly as it had appeared. He spoke.

"Do you smoke?" He paused for what I assume he thought was dramatic effect. "Wacky Backy?"

Wacky Backy? What the fuck was that? It sounded like Yogi Bear's sophisticated city cousin who'd popped down to Jellystone Park to try and prove to Boo-Boo that he was smarter than the average motherfucker. Somewhere in the back of my mind, Jefferson Airplane started to play White Rabbit, filtering everything else, like out man. They were pulling a by the numbers good cop, bad cop routine. Kojak and The Sweeney had a lot to answer for.

"If you are referring to Marijuana sir, the answer

is no."

Another lie. I began to consider a career in politics. These clowns barely flickered at the best of times. One of the "Beautiful" people was obviously behind the curtain, turning the screws of my discomfort

"Are you sure?"

Hadn't they heard about Nancy's campaign? Or tuned into the Grange Hill anthem that was written after Zammo was discovered smacked out on the floor of a dirty toilet? No means fucking no.

"I'm sure sir. Even if I did wouldn't I be right in thinking that outside of the school it isn't any of your concern?"

Number one leaned forward on his desk. Come on, tell me you've got some evidence and Jimmy the Greek has given me up.

"Perhaps...though we could always express our concern to your parents."

"What if they don't mind, sir?"

Again, I really was off in the realms of fantasy this time. But what they don't know can't hurt them right?

"Then boy, I truly worry about your future."

I'm sure you do, just like you worry about the next ice age.

"Can I go now?"

Just you try and stop my fly Huggy Bear self from strutting out of here you tired, old Starsky and

Hutch clichés.

"Get out of my sight".

Walking out of there, I was determined to try and find out who had set me up and kick the ever living shit out of them. Unfortunately, like most of the promises I made to myself back then, I didn't get around to it and things returned to the way they had always been, but not the way they would be. A couple of years later I ran into some of the "Beautiful" people again, and the dark clouds lifted from my bad day. Had they been infected by humility? No way, but they were all working shit jobs and trying to relive their "glory days". I couldn't do anything that hadn't already been done. Ain't life a bitch? Karma catches you in the end and what goes around, comes around. A debt can last a lifetime, but it'll always get paid in the end. Knowing your place and staying in it are two very different things. Oh, and if you make it through the hard times relatively unscathed? Stay tuned and change to whatever channel you want to be.

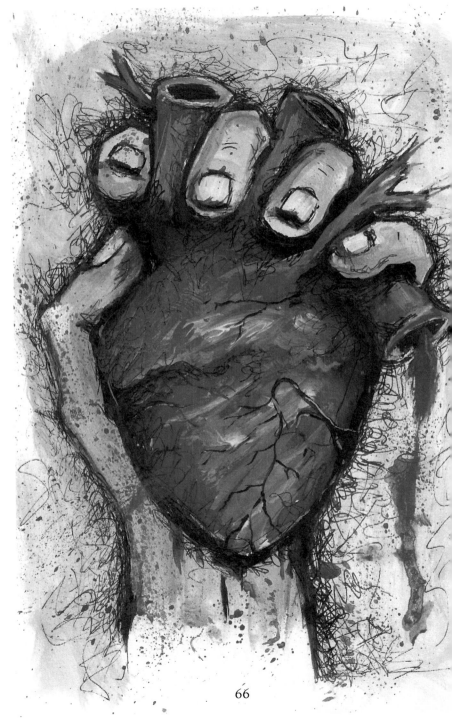

11

Intermission

I think about you all the time, suppressing my murderous intent, keeping it hidden. It focuses my energy, festering as it poisons my being. I mark the passing of each day by creating a different scenario in which I claim my vengeance. A blood oath soaked by innocents, a stain which tattoos you for eternity. Stare into the void and you'll find me, staring back at you, the blackness of forever sealing every avenue of escape. You are mine, a thing to be played with, broken and left to rot, putrefying in the cold vacuum where there was once a heart.

I can wait. Wait for you to forget that I was ever part of your world. When the time comes you will experience the pain that is mine. Bursting through your door, I kiss you, sucking the air from the middle of your chest. Your lips turn blue as you weakly try to dislodge me, I bite down, feeling the heat as your blood splashes against my neck I spit your lying tongue into your face. As you double over in a desperate attempt to regain the severed muscle, I kick you hearing your ribs shatter with each successive blow. You're on your side now, battling for air as your lungs fill with liquid and collapse. I piss on you and the urine mixes with the blood still oozing from your mouth, the scent of retribution summoning the shadow of death. Do you even feel my knife enter your stomach? I remove your organs with surgical precision, label them and show you each one in turn. You expire in your own faeces and blood, your life remembered by no one. That was easy wasn't it?

I can wait.

12

It's Happy Hour Again

It would have been so easy to walk away, leave them to it and let them sort their own bloody mess out. But I couldn't do it. I don't know what stopped me. Foolish pride, a stubborn refusal to quit or just plain old stupidity, something made me put my head on the chopping block. What had started as a magnificent concept had quickly backfired and covered everyone involved in crap from the waist up. Put us in a line up and we'd have been identified straight away and sentenced by the best laid plans of mice and men before any legal representation arrived.

A new club had opened in my hometown, and as with all new clubs it had soon become the place to be seen in. If you weren't there, then where the fuck were you, you useless nobody? Get hip and make the triple jump from obscurity to happening. This club was different though, they wanted to create a drug free atmosphere in which all the patrons could enjoy themselves. Now the more cynical among you will whine on about how such a policy would only be implemented to increase beer sales and exempt the management from prosecution if someone overdosed on their premises. True, but for once the management wasn't motivated by profit. All they wanted was a safe haven for people to blow off steam and have a good time. They called in the "experts". They called in me. The drug and alcohol agency where I worked was summoned to advise them on the problem and investigate how such a proposition could be made to work and being a local I could blend in, become just another face in the crowd and assess the situation from the "inside".

The whole operation, to my sheer disbelief, appeared to be running exactly as it had been planned. I turned up week after week and did what I'd been asked to, which was spy on the patrons and squeal to the bouncers about where the shit was going down and leave them to do the rest and then finish each evening by drinking myself into oblivion. It was money for old rope. Any business-man worth his salt will tell you to look for an opening in the market and when you find it, pounce, fangs barred in preparation to chew on the fat of the land. Acting on the advice of his own snitches, the Muscle that had already moved into property elsewhere in the town, saw his chance and invested in shares to make the club his own. Without thinking I'd set up the deal of the century and paved the way for him to slide right in. My easy gig had passed its sell by date and all hell was about to break loose.

As with all hard cases, his reputation preceded

him, and as he tried to enter the club that night, Management was waiting for him. They stared each other down, gun fighters at high noon, each waiting for the other to make his move before responding in an appropriate manner. The Muscle was handed a card by his opponent, which warned the reader of the dangers of drug abuse, a shock tactic designed to alarm rather than educate, as skirmishes were fought by whatever means were deemed necessary. Forced into a corner before he could begin to irrigate another building with his narcotics, the Muscle replied, using the only method he had ever mastered. He lashed out, his head connecting solidly with that of his welcoming committee, the cut opening up before the action was even completed. The Management lay on the floor bleeding and the Muscle stood over him letting him know what he thought of both his club and his policy before being forced out of the door by the resident doormen, who were, as usual, too late to do anything useful. Some things are the same the world over. One final thing had to be done and as he left, the Muscle pointed at me and winked letting me know that he knew what my role had been and who I was. Fuck, I thought that the plastic tree had obscured me from his line of sight. I had nowhere to run and nowhere to hide. It was my time and when your number's up, there isn't a single thing you can do about it.

Every time I went anywhere for the next three months I looked over my shoulder, ready to receive the beating that was mine for the taking. Not that I'm afraid of taking a kicking now and then, that's the way of things, it reminds you that the strong prey on the weak. Pain is a frame of mind, and when you accept it for what it is, it no longer becomes a conscious problem. Of course, I had the option of turning him over to John Q Law, but I hadn't ratted anyone out before, and wasn't about to start because I was a little scared. My professional pride was at stake, and I wasn't going to throw it away because I was worried about a bit of the old ultra violence. I had to work in this field, hold my head up and gain people's trust. No fucking way was I going to be a stoolie, a bitch for the man with no code or honour. If it was coming, bring it on.

I think it was around this time that I realised that crime had become a game of intimidation and that he who had the best brief would win the day. Intimidation I can take, throw it my way until the cow comes back from one of her round trips to the moon. Even the terror tactics had changed, instead of their fists the thugs now used sales techniques, smiling and selling you their side of the story, making sure that you understood what was on the line without resorting to threats of violence. Caught between a rock and a hard place, the prosecuting slime and defence sludge, it was easier for me to forget that I'd seen anything out of the ordinary that Saturday night. It was simply business as usual. The court case passed and I still don't know what happened. Ashamed of my chicken shit attitude, I couldn't bring myself to ask. Still, it was nice to know that some things are the way they've always been. Winning is everything and nice guys always finish last. Go team, go!

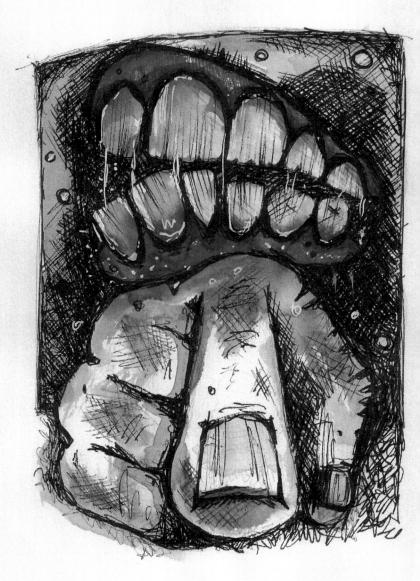

13

Travelling Man

"How far will you go?"

Silence. With a single question the entire room stopped. Dead.

"How far will you go?"

I looked up, smiling, unable to understand how such a penetrating remark could have come from someone who had spent his entire life cradled in the loving arms of his family, twisted and corrupted by the decaying values of a generation that had died before it was even born.

"How far will you go?"

The answer emerged before I'd even considered the question, before the words had created the necessary image I needed to process and rip the statement apart. No time for a quick one liner, a clever put down or bullshit macho bravado. It was out. No time. That's all there was to it and in the words of the eternal poet, it was my first and last mistake.

"Further than you will ever know or could possibly dream of."

I'd been at the university for three hours and already felt trapped by the confining walls of academia. No matter where you go, or how far you travel, a school is still a school. The smell gives it away. Dank, dark, depressing, the stench of death all neatly wrapped up and presented to those good little boys and girls who had obeyed the rules, followed the guidelines and studied hard enough to be told

"You're the future, the top 10%, the cream of the crop. Study, absorb and become part of the collective. You can't be happy unless you're part of the machine, cogs turning, gears meshing, everything moving in perfect harmony."

It was a crock of shit, a bubbling cauldron that reeked of hypocrisy, weakness and deceit. Why bother? If I'd been a crafty fellow, and it's never been one of my virtues, I'd have mumbled something about fulfilment of potential and the obvious need for a college education in the ever decreasing employment market. You needed every advantage you could get and every opportunity to stamp on your opponent in the land of competition. Unfortunately, the truth was a lot easier to digest. I needed a place to hide out, lay low and plan my next move.

My first day at school was being repeated, only this time I was ready for it. In the eyes of the law, I was an adult, whatever the fuck that is, who was able to legally buy beer and get cheap hand jobs from middle aged whores in back street massage parlours. Breath in, breath out. It still smelled like school, but what the hell? If you don't try, then you can't complain and the right to air a grievance is a guaranteed right of democracy, Gods damn it.

I paid for my coffee, lit a cigarette and stared at the animals I'd spend the next three years of my life with. The usual mix of would-be business vampires planning corporate takeovers, athletic freaks pumped on steroid cocktails, lost sheep separated from the herd quietly bleating for help and "alternative" types already busy trying to be cooler than the next man, waiting to be noticed and revered, shuffled around each other in ever decreasing circles. Maybe it wouldn't be so bad, everyone was in the same boat after all, strangers reaching out in the darkness. Social misfits all trying to row an empty vessel with one arm tied behind their backs. Kick back, relax. Don't show any fear or they'll descend like a pack of ravenous hyenas and serve you up with an apple in your mouth and a stick up your arse, slowly roasted over a barbecue. Want a beer with your slice of suburban white male?

Places were found, circles formed and conversations begun. In the space of a half hour, I knew six life stories, each one less interesting than the one it followed, built on a foundation of exaggeration, embellishment and pulp fiction. Listen, but don't open your mouth, the less they knew about me the better it'd be for all concerned. They couldn't hurt me if they didn't have any ammunition. As always, the conversation turned to sex and music, the acceptable faces of youth culture, and as vague innuendos were exchanged it became obvious that the previous summer's teaching manuals had been the popular music press and the Karma Sutra. Through the haze of smoke the mating rituals began, and the taste of twelve hour coffee started to make every nerve twitch and muscle spasm.

Question. Bang. Answer. Boom.

"You're a fucking liar, I don't believe you and I'm sure no one else does either."

Convicted by a judge without the aid of a jury. I stared at my accuser, wearing the clothes his mother had bought for him before packing him off, tears streaming from her eyes. He pushed his spectacles further up his nose and focused on the core of my being, watching, begging for anything, scratching for any shred of proof that would enable him to climb another rung on the pathetic social ladder that the Pepsi generation placed so much faith in. There would be no satisfaction this day, or any other. All it needed was a casual shrug.

"That's your problem, you deal with it and frankly I couldn't give a flying fuck if you believe me or you don't."

The conversation should have ended then and there and the file should have been closed, If only everything in life was that simple. The end point reversed and stoked the boiler of self-hatred that had been built up through years of humiliation and constant self-abuse.

Deflated, he backed down, stared at the floor and never spoke another word to me. His spirit was already crushed and his success guaranteed. Moulded from day one, we are all supposed to accept what we're told, blindly pushing forward, with no concept of hope and no hope for the future. University had become another word for bureaucracy and knowledge was a forbidden weapon. There were no lessons left to learn and no goals worth chasing. If anything was going to change it wouldn't be on this path, a straight road to the centre of automation with no possibility of parole. I had seen the future and couldn't put a name to the face of my guide to the inevitable reality that awaits us all. Consumption of caffeine and idle chatter continued, but in a single after-noon the cards had been dealt and you've got to play the hand you're given. I never was any good at poker.

82

14

So Long Hope, Hello Oblivion

Tick tock, tick tock. Hands moving around a face, sand slipping through an hourglass, it doesn't matter how you describe it, the passage of time is one of the only things humanity can truly depend on. It won't slow down, it won't speed up, but it will snap at your heels until you let your guard down and then..."wham"! It'll jump up and bite you on the down belows and danglers. It's a point of fact that when you're dead, you're fucking dead. Nada, nothing, finito. The fat lady has sung the final chorus and Elvis has left the building.

Up and down four flights of stairs, morning, noon and night. Different faces, but the same, singular monotone voice, gently inducing an already drowsy audience into the blissfully unaware land of make believe that controls all everyday actions.

"Repent for the end is nigh, all will be cast down on an even scale".

Awake. They all look the same. New age philosophers regurgitating, politically correct idealism with an injection of pathetic humour, because hey, they're only human and just two steps ahead of our mammalian brethren. Tutors, lecturers, teachers, call them what you will, they all stand united with a common objective. To nurture and cultivate a garden of useless information in the barren minds of fresh victims. A thing of beauty, transplanted and implanted, then passed on to the next poor schmuck waiting in line.

During one of these up and down trips that all blurred into a single journey as the minutes flew away, waving as they disappeared over the horizon, a switch was flicked on and I remembered a documentary about quadrupeds. Scampering around, licking the shit off each other's fur. The people teaching me about life, the universe and everything became the subterranean creatures, slipping into the real world only when necessary, hiding in the college walls, a familiar place in which to hibernate and vegetate. They were just like the rest of us, scared to face the world, to stand up and scream.

"Fuck you, you can beat me down, but I'll be back with a bigger grin on my face each time."

What horrors had they seen? What had forced them to retreat to the halls of enlightenment?

I knew, at last, that I stood as an equal with any man or woman who tried to point me in the right direction. If knowledge was power, what were these fuckers doing here? The world lay at their feet, yet they turned their backs on it, preferring theory to practice, shut away in a fortress of solitude. Theoretical debate never fed a starving child or brought superpowers to a conference table. At last a common thread from which I could spin a web to sit upon in the prevailing calm as the hurricane blew outside. Each day I smiled as they discussed social revolutions, animal genetics, feminism, anthropology, statistics and criminal psychology. The more I learned, the more I lost. It poured from every orifice, and the more I tried to plug the holes, the bigger the leaks became.

You know that straw that broke the camel's back and the old wives' tale about old dogs and new tricks? I used to think they were harmless fables designed to besiege and capture the weak minded, but the truth is that they were just facets on the twenty sided die of fate, the polyhedron on which each face is just another way to fuck you over, and sooner or later you're going to have to roll it.

I found myself sitting across a desk from one of these people that I felt an affinity with, the bond strengthened by my cowardice and inability to choose which road to travel.

"Do you like the course you're doing? Is everything okay?"

Pseudo empathy flowed from him and I could see that he was dying for a chance to play a game of social workers and downtrodden. If there'd been more people in the room he'd have called for a group hug, asked us what it was like to be in the womb and pretend to be trees bending in a summer breeze. He was mine and I was going to play him like a fiddle until the strings broke. The best form of defence is a good defence and when you've got your opponent on the ropes, you should always go for the throat and rip his fucking windpipe out.

My mouth opened. Nothing happened. It opened again. And again. Something was wrong. I was stuck doing an impression of marine life for a non-paying customers' viewing pleasure. I checked every neurone I could and my psychological V8 appeared to be firing in perfect order.

"I hadn't thought about it before now."

Shit, in a punk rock minute, I'd given the game away. I'd lurched into a clearance sale and every single item had to go.

"That's what I thought. You don't seem to be fitting in very well."

Fuck, this guy was a master and had every base covered. I only had one option left. Anger.

Motherfucker had just called me a misfit and a screw up. Why didn't he tell me something I didn't already know, and while he was at it, grab me a coffee to go. My key was in the ignition and I was under starter's orders.

"Look let's just cut the shit. You came here because it seemed like a good idea at the time and you didn't know what else to do. Right?"

I nodded and my jaw dropped open again. Someone should have wired that motherfucker shut. Tight.

He leaned back in his chair, smiling and gently touched the wall with his shoulders.

"See this is no kind of place to be in if you don't want to. You're wasting everybody's time, and time is too precious a commodity to waste. If you don't want to come in don't, but find out what you do want to do. Don't talk about it, do it. Understand?"

Uh huh. My head nodded in time with my heartbeat, which has slowed down to an occasional thud.

"One last thing. Don't be a teacher and don't join the police and you should be okay. Shut the door behind you on your way out."

I stood up, turned around, walked out the door and down those stairs. My fate in the hands of the gods, I walked into the sun. Minutes passed. Freedom had never felt better.

15

The Thoroughly Modern Savant

I'll admit it, I'm one of those poor wretches who bad mouths his country, lounges around listening to rock and roll and continually babbles about a fictitious revolution. Yeah, I've burnt the flag, I've even wiped my arse with it − believe me, it's no substitute for soft toilet paper and it makes you itch like buggery, but it didn't do any good as the useless rag is still being purchased by people like George and Mabel from Bumfuck, Idaho and Japanese tourists trying to savour every second of the British experience.

Let me tell you about the British experience. It's fucking dull, with a capital "D". A fourth rate banana republic without the weather, filled with soccer hooligans obsessed with the good old days and the glory of a long dead empire, whose only contributions to global culture have been tea and scones and warm beer. Excuse me while I get all excited and worked up about nothing.

Excitement. That's what rebellion and protest are supposed to be about, stirring up the dust that complacency leaves in its wake, ushering in the new ideas while taking a shit on the old, and leaving the opposition covered in excrement while you come up smelling of roses. Music has long embodied the voice of disenchanted youth, a cry for help from a wilderness overgrown by corruption, bigotry and vice, a force to be used for good, that's heard above the confused discord of wheeler dealing and personal ambition. A tool to cut away the ties that bound us to a hopeless future. But we were never going to get very far with a dull, rusted blade that hasn't been sharpened since it was first used fifty years ago.

Nineteen sixty-seven, the summer of love was a fairy tale told by lazy hippies, more interested in dropping acid and expanding their minds to reach across cosmic barriers than being heard. In the right hands a solitary thought can be a dangerous weapon, but the Children of the Revolution dropped the ball when they discovered Albert Hoffman's miraculous mind fuck. They must have had governments shaking in their boots. The only reason Woodstock worked was because nobody thought it would and trying to repeat that happy accident only opened the floor to corporate sponsorship. Would Hendrix have worn a Pepsi logo? Guess we'll never know; he took door number three along with his amigos as soon as the going got a little rough. What about the people who had kept the wheels in motion? They stood up to be counted with the system, part of the very thing they swore that they wanted nothing to do with, swapping caftans and love beads for BMWs when they became accountants and lawyers. Peace? I hope you choke on it.

The nature of the beast is always transforming itself, replacing trends and fashions almost as fast as the factories can produce them. Heavy metal appeared and invited all the morons to the ball, giving themselves whiplash and self-inflicted brain haemorrhages as they banged the night away to their favourite tunes. And all of those lyrics about Satan and why every woman wanted to jump the writer's bones while strung out on eight balls and cheap whiskey really did an incredible job of shaking the foundations of society and helping to expose the system for the enduring farce that it is. Breeding a nation of idiots couldn't have been easier. It was escapism as its absolute pinnacle, that diverted the listener's attention away from the mundanity it allowed them to become part of. Nobody cared, the bands got their money and the kids worked a standard week in order to buy the latest tour shirt. Accessorise, they had to learn to accessorise, cover themselves in patches sewn on to dirty denim jackets, stained by the sweat of slave labour. Everything had to be cranked louder than hell so that they could drown reason in screeching guitars, thundering drums and piercing vocals. It's like where it's at dude.

Ghetto's rose up and threw their fury at authority in the form of rap and hip hop, painting a picture of life on the poor side of town. You had to be badder than the next guy; if he'd killed five people, then you had to have dispatched at least twice as many. Life was hard at the bottom, but black and white came together, colour became irrelevant as the artists rightly pointed out that they were better than their surroundings. Money flowed and music became a career opportunity. You didn't have to stay down and take shit; you could do something about it, improving your situation as you did so. Just as the pieces appeared to be fitting together, the fly landed in the ointment. Instead of helping each other and co-operating to ensure that they left something better, the musicians started killing each other again.

"Yo Tupac, you said some things that I didn't like very much. They upset me, hurt my feelings, so I'm gonna kill you good and proper."

How does the saying go? You can take the man from the ghetto, but you can't take the ghetto from the man. When Pac died, hope died with him.

All that was left was Suburbia and its adopted regime, punk rock. Drop out and fight the fucking system, act your rage and show them your anger. Punkers, we're worse than any of the others, so fragmented that we couldn't even unite to fight our way out of a paper bag. Those of us who didn't piss our lives away with a tube of glue, a bottle of cider and a needle and spoon, invented a million subcultures instead of embracing the whole. Woe betide any newcomers to the scene, it's holier than thou and you can't enter if you haven't got the right password. After all, if punk became too popular, people might have to take us seriously, and we can't have that can we? We're our own worst enemies. Society one, punk rock zero.

Rebellion? It's an old man's game. The real rebels are the desk bound lifers who defraud their companies, beavering away behind closed doors and bucking, breaking and subverting the norm through the power of invisible white power crime. Fight the power and buy a top forty record. It's the only alternative left.

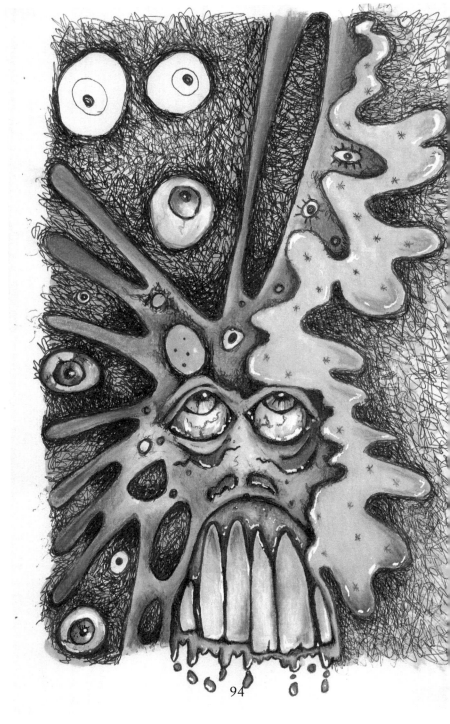

16

Pharmaceutical Evolution

There were four of us. Mean motherfuckers to a man, ripped on the inside and poisoned on the out, waiting for something to happen. If you'd looked up the definition of under-achiever in the Oxford Alternative English Dictionary a picture of the four of us would have stared back at you, dicks in hands, dancing to the beat of a different drummer. We were the remnants of a gene pool contaminated by crass commercialism and the "me" generation. The last drop that trickled down the leg of multinational trade-offs. Each of us was a loser, proud of the fact that society had left us to play the game with an incomplete rule book. There wasn't anybody to tuck us in at night and read us a bedtime story, the thread of chemical escapism was our nurse maid, chasing away monsters and exorcising evil spirits, putting her arms around us, drawing us closer to her bosom as the outside world surrounded us. Left to our own devices the kitchen sink had become a melting pot for physical science. Reconstituting hallucinogenics and tobacco as a psychedelic exit from reality that lit up like a Christmas tree every time its plastic coffin was touched. For weeks we'd caressed the containing vessel dreaming of the alternative realities that waited beyond the veil. The ceremony was about to begin. War paint was applied and head dresses fixed in place, each of us stared deeply into the flames, drawing our own conclusions as we pondered the implications of our impending journey. Standing as one with the night, held by the velvet curtain of darkness, illuminated only by the sparks that rode currents of disparity as they drifted from the fire.

The pipe, delicately carved by the warped hands of a twisted imagination, was passed around. Cold to the touch, its warmth soon became apparent to even the most distant animals, a thing of beauty in a world of misery. Its existence proved that man walked the path of destiny alone, diseased and condemned to obscurity. I held it, gently running my fingers up and down its stem, and thought about Duke sitting alone in Woodstock watching home movies, reliving his memories, time and time again. Through the smoke I watched my demons play hide and seek, holding hands as they carved their initials on the bark of long dead trees. I lifted the tube to my mouth, lit the bowl, inhaled slowly and felt the burning fumes scar my lungs as the toxins entered my bloodstream and took my brain apart, piece by piece. My senses packed their bags and headed for the coast, leaving friends, family and familiarity behind as they searched for a place in the country far from the vapid hustle of small town life. I sat in the bleachers with a hot dog and a beer, Plato to my left, Aristotle to my right and watched the world as its history flashed by in three innings.

The dinosaurs followed all of Mother Nature's guidelines and looked like they were doing pretty well. Swing batter, swing. Strike one, they got themselves a healthy dose of religion and started fighting, each side claiming that God had made them in his image and as such was superior to the others. Strike two came with the free love movement, as Tyrannosaur humped Brontosaurus and vice versa. The air became filled with the stench of cheap swamp aftershave as safe sex was cast aside due to increasing rubber and pharmaceutical costs, and badly controlled pesticides made even the most virile Stegosaur sterile. Strike three. With the discovery of nicotine and virtual reality the terrible lizards disappeared almost without trace. Only the mammals remained, content and happy in their work as salesmen and insurance brokers, they had never understood the need to let their fur down.

Rain stopped play as the apes evolved, arguing over, and about, anything and everything that sprung to mind at any given moment. What started as a dispute over a bedroom extension soon developed into full blown tribal warfare, the boundaries being drawn over every monkey's right to fit mirrored ceilings in his bathroom. If you didn't like your neighbour you moved in order to let your inner child grow, finding the room to nurture those nagging design concepts like the wheel and the arrowhead. The economy collapsed as ape after ape gave in to the new age fanaticism and political extremes that shook the earth to its molten crust.

The future rested on team communication in the final inning. Scientific theory put forward its case as did theology, philosophy, sociology and a million other minor plays. With no decided game plan or common consensus, the entire team was soon struck out, tripping over their own laces on the way to the home plate. The field was abandoned as ten thousand fans grudgingly made their way home, muttering and cursing the fact that stupidity had cost the visiting team an almost certain victory. Lights dimmed as the staff set about preparing the ball park for the next evening, crossing their fingers and praying that the home side's winning streak would hold. A mountain of food wrappers and empty paper cups were the only testament to the evening's game.

I woke to find my hair matted together by pieces of the previous evening's meal, my war paint smudged and my tattered jeans stained by urine. Spitting in a vain attempt to rid myself of the smell and taste of rancid vomit, I sat in the damp grass desperately trying to warm my hands over the smouldering remains of the fire. If any of us are masters of our own fate, then belly up to the bar and have another drink, because closing time is getting closer. While you're there, have one for me. Its happy hour, the juke box is rocking and the umpire's decision is final.

17

Pay-Per-View In The Poconos

Everybody said he had it coming. One way or another he was going to get his arse handed to him on a plate and for his own sake the lesson had to be learned sooner rather than later. Five weeks of his constant companionship had driven me to the edge of insanity and my blood began to boil every time he opened his mouth. Stuck in the middle of the boondocks, sharing a wooden cabin with my fellow counsellor and a pack of screaming kids, had pushed me off the cliffs and the scattered rocks of madness were the only things left to break my fall. Fuck, it had sounded so easy. Take care of some rich brats for a couple of months while their parents toured Europe with their credit cards, foaming at the mouth in anticipation of ethnic bargains. I'd borne witness to a television programme about the summer camp experience in which fat children were sent there to lose weight by fair means or foul. The parents didn't care how they dropped the pounds, as long as they shed them in record time, because chunky children can't help you climb social ladders. Denied sugar products and forced to exercise the blimps cracked, one by one, promising anything in exchange for a chocolate bar. It was passive-aggressive torture at its most refined and it looked like it could be fun. Like most things, it had been blown out of all proportion by propaganda and the network's need for entertaining programming. When I arrived at my designated camp, there were no fat children to persecute, just normal, healthy, average kids obsessed with bad hip hop and the only pleasure left was in taunting those abandoned youngsters who longed for the comforts of familiar surroundings.

"I want my mommy and daddy. I want to go home."

"Shut up kid. Mommy and Daddy don't love you anymore. They've traded you in for a new model. You're going to stay here with me, forever. Won't that be fun?"

My fellow counsellor had started as he meant to go on, full of, among other things, sickening false sincerity. He loved everyone and nothing seemed to annoy him, apart from the vices I revelled in, displaying his disapproval at every available opportunity. All the goodwill and well meant gestures of this angelic soul couldn't excuse the basic fact that he was a dick and completely incapable of doing the job he was hired to do. I mean, who ever heard of a lifeguard who didn't like to get his feet wet? Every single day he'd stand on the jetty of the purpose built lake, blowing his whistle and pointing at anything that moved. Blowing his stupid fucking whistle over and over and over again. I began to hear it in my sleep and imagined myself standing over him, forcing a pillow on to his face, counting down from two thousand, waiting for his shallow chest contractions and snoring to end. It would have been merciful release and would have ended his suffering and mine. Or I'd end up shoving that damn whistle so far down his fucking throat, that he'd play musical chairs every time he broke wind. It wasn't just his phoney ass demeanour and dedication to his "work"; I could probably have lived with those defects. Probably. He couldn't even understand the simplest instructions. If you told him one thing, he'd do another. Everything about him screamed future social worker. The world wouldn't miss him.

There's only so much any man can take, and another rainy day schedule had forced us to participate in finger painting and ceramics for beginners, which was almost as much fun as drinking paint. Kids want destruction, not the sort of new age crafts that are taught to the homicidal maniacs who spend their days vacationing in various institutions across the United States. The generation gap was growing wider by the hour. Today though, was going to be different. We'd been sent to the martial arts studio, a tumbledown old shack lined with crash mats and a few pairs of sparring gloves. Usually we'd just encourage the kids to play, turn cartwheels, do handstands and the sort of positive movement that was apparently designed to enhance their development. But all they wanted to do was fight. Violence was in and Mr Rogers was dead in the water. As I'd always been taught to lead by example and never let anyone do something that you were not prepared to do yourself, I put a pair of the gloves on and watched my "partner" do the same as he limbered up with a series of idiotic callisthenics. You put your right leg in, your left leg out and beat the crap out of any motherfucker in your way. One of the children pretended to be a ring bell and it was seconds out, Round One. My nemesis in camp counselling flew at me, wind milling his arms, flailing, his eyes closed. I couldn't believe what I was seeing and stood rooted to the spot, frozen in mock amusement. His first blow caught me straight between the legs and warm, all too familiar nausea rose up from my stomach and made my knees buckle.

"Calm down man, we're only messing around!"

He blanked me and walked away, smiling. The human bell rang again and it was time for Round Two – and the same thing happened again. He flailed his arms, ran straight at me and cracked me right in the testicles. I tasted the rubber of the crash mat, which was more palatable than half of the junk food that I'd been served since taking on this fucking job.

"Do that again and I'll drop you. I swear to God."

He grinned, held his arms in the air in triumph and strolled over to his corner of the mat.

The bell rang again and again, his arms flailed, his eyes closed and he charged forward. I guess he figured that when you were ahead, there was no point in fucking with a winning formula. The cries of our audience had reached fever pitch and they were screaming for blood and carnage. I couldn't disappoint them, could I? I stood my ground and waited until he came closer and hit him square in the middle of his face. Something gave way, followed by a crunching sound that was similar to a dog finishing off a bone. He hit the mat, blood flowing between the clumsy grip of the over sized gloves he wore, and assumed a foetal position, making gurgling, crying noises. Four places. I'd broken his nose in four places. He packed his stuff and left when he returned from the hospital, spurred on by embarrassment. I wish that I could say that the punch made me feel better, or that it had been well aimed and on target, but it was an accident. It was a fluke. Just like some men's greatest achievements. And twenty years later, I still have nightmares about hitting him, about lashing out instead of trying to sit down and find a way to resolve our seemingly petty, and insignificant, "insurmountable" differences. Be careful what you wish for, you just might get it.

18

Sex, Guns And Rock 'N' Roll

We decided, as mature adults do, to sit down and discuss the more fulfilling moments of our lives, what we felt we'd achieved and what those achievements meant to each of us. What the hell, it would help to pass another afternoon in what was turning out to be a long and uneventful summer. A grown up spin the bottle with no forfeits and no fear of retaliation. I stroked my glass, one of those ice branded beers that city businessmen place so much faith in but taste no different to any other overpriced beverage. Special brewing techniques aside, the advertising industry has a lot to answer for. I waited for my turn. It came all too soon.

"I taught American children how to shoot. I was a riflery instructor on one of the summer camps that kids go to during their school holidays."

I don't think that I'd ever thought about it before that moment, or even considered in my wildest dreams the possibility that my actions might have long term consequences. To me it was just something I'd picked up due to an obsessive childhood interest in the armed forces. I'd joined one of those paramilitary groups for teenagers, a kind of Hitler Youth for the post war years designed to keep an even flow of disposable cannon fodder signing their lives away for king and country. They were supposed to teach discipline and instil self-confidence, but all it really did was breed a growing resentment for authority figures of all shapes and sizes. The only thing I'd ever learnt to do while passing through their ranks, with any degree of proficiency, was use a rifle. Instead of the targets, I'd seen my teachers from school, the fucked apes that had beaten me to a pulp on a regular basis and the blue uniforms, and it hadn't been that hard. I qualified as a marksman with ease and won many a useless prize in travelling carnivals. To tell you the truth, I'd forgotten all about it having quit the pseudo-fascist corps due my lack of progress up the ladder of seniority which was, in turn, directly attributable to a bad attitude. Then it became my golden ticket to a summer of freedom in the USA. Overnight I returned to the habits of old and dusted off my uniform while choking on the moth balls.

Two months of teaching children to shoot at bits of paper was no problem, I could do it standing on my head. Admittedly, there were a few grievances, pre civil war rifles that were eventually held together by masking tape, rounds that misfired nine times out of ten and a gargoyle called Evan, a second hand car salesman's heir with a fondness for golf pants and unloading every single round he could at my head. If you've never felt the breeze that a bullet creates as it passes within three inches of your skull, then you're missing out. It's an experience that you can well do without. Apart from those minor glitches, my time on the range finished without any major incidents, all the participants were awarded a certificate to pin above their beds and everyone went their own merry way.

It took eighteen months for me to realise what I'd done, the hammer only hitting me as I sat in that dingy bar shooting the shit with virtual strangers. I'd walked into one of the most violent countries on the face of the planet and encouraged its sons and daughters to bear arms, a right that was theirs, guaranteed by the very constitution under which they lived. Nobody played war anymore, it was a cold reality, the streets were a battlefield and none of the soldiers were old enough to even buy a packet of cigarettes. You could be killed for walking into the wrong neighbourhood. The morality of the situation wasn't important because that was just the way it was, a code by which someone lived and died every twelve and a half seconds. I started dreaming about Evan, saw him wearing a red bandanna, leaning out of the window of a car crawling down a dimly lit street, squeezing the trigger of a semi-automatic weapon, his rag doll targets falling on each other as their fragile bodies were pulverised by hot lead. The shell cases lay in the gutter surrounding an overturned tricycle, a birthday present that would be idle forever more. It haunted my nights, the same image, over and over. Evan grinned at me, a blood soaked flag cloaking his shoulders.

"Look at what you've turned me into you mercenary prick. Look at what I've become. I hope you enjoyed yourself."

I scoured the papers every day, hoping to see a story about the gang warfare that plagued the barrios, praying that I wouldn't see a familiar face whose actions were my indirect responsibility. They say that if something doesn't happen on your doorstep, then you shouldn't worry about it, it's not your fault and there is nothing you can do about it. It doesn't help me to sleep at night though, knowing that I might have helped someone to die, knowing that a mother might have lost a son or a daughter because I wanted a cheap vacation. Knowing that someone wouldn't grow old, wouldn't feel the warmth of lying next to a partner on a winter night or watch their dreams come to fruition. Hey everyone, I'm the guy who killed the cure for cancer and put medical research back twenty-five years. Of course, I can't be sure that any of these things have happened and this is a worse case scenario. But what in life is certain? Here today, gone tomorrow, everything changes when you're looking down the barrel of a gun. May your gods have mercy on my sleazy soul, because when I'm dead and gone, it'll be Evan who ushers me through the gates of Hell.

19

The Criminal High Life

I looked over at Doug as he turned the key in the ignition and grinned.

"Let's do it."

Ahead of us lay the Canadian border and we had all the time in the world in which to exert our manly authority on the North West frontier. It was the moment we'd been waiting for all summer. The good times were within our grasp, just minutes away, and there was only one chasm left to cross. How to get past the imposing Canucks with a full cargo of beer and cigarettes. Deciding that our best approach would be to charge straight through and hope to hell that they didn't want to look in the boot, we inched forward as another apple pie family were waved on without collecting two hundred pounds or proceeding directly to the Big House. A list of regulations towered above the driver's side window, the first commandment standing out, written in bold, black capital letters.

"Thou shall declare all alcohol or tobacco products".

Pay the tax or take our chances? Fuck it, we'd already paid once and had followed the rules of capitalism to the letter. A man's property is his own and possession is nine-tenths of the law, and we had earned the right to drink cold Buds on humid Canadian nights. It was one that we fully intended to exercise. No moustached symbol of authority in a red clown outfit and cowboy hat was going to deny us that privilege, although how we intended to stop them confiscating our contraband wasn't on the list of topics that we'd discussed as we rolled up to the border. Wine, women and sin, yes. How to put a wrestling hold on a mounted policeman? Not so much...

The Canadian trip, and the thought of it, was the only thing that had helped me to maintain my sanity during my tour of duty as riflery instructor on a New England summer camp. Days off were spent in training for what had become known as "The Special Olympics", the drinking marathon that we planned to start as soon as we crossed the border. Practice sessions had been few and far between, and held in such diverse locations as New York City and Philadelphia, but gradually my right arm stamina had increased as had my capacity for alcohol. I had also learnt how easy it was to corrupt young minds with a weekly radio programme that held on-air discussions and interviews with the strangest counsellors we could find (secret transvestites and Marxist Leninists were hard to come by in Pennsylvania) and played nothing but punk rock; Black Flag, The Minutemen, The Dead Milkmen, Fugazi, you name them, we spun them. With each broadcast, our challenge drew closer. The final day of camp came; we said our goodbyes, threw our shit in the car and headed off into the sunset. Picking up supplies was a matter of confidence. A fake ID and false smile will carry you through the most arduous of beer runs, and I'd been taught the upside-down frown by professionals. It's the first thing you're taught when you arrive at one of the fortresses that litter the American countryside, smile and be happy when faced with adversity. When a child kicks you, smile and gently reprimand him. Then you wait until after lights out and beat the shit out of the little fucker with a bar of soap wrapped in a towel. Bend the rules, don't break them, and there's nothing you can't do. Compared to the devil spawn I'd cared for, convincing liquor store owners that I was old enough to buy their product was a stroll in the park.

Mister Nails, a perfect advertisement for the Canadian Board of Tourism, knocked on the door, trying to peer inside the car. Obligingly, Doug rolled down his window, nervously fingering his documents.

"Passports."

Both were handed over for a cursory examination, which I'm sure would have included dusting for fingerprints and DNA testing had they the resources and time needed for such essential checks.

"Reason for entering Canada. Business or pleasure?"

Shit. Which category did the Olympics fall under? Seeing as it was an independent event, the later seemed more appropriate.

"Pleasure."

"Do you have somewhere to stay for the duration of your visit?"

Yeah, the athlete's village. They've reserved a suite with cable television for us. Hey, we're the only contenders, so it's nothing but the best for us.

"Yes sir, we're staying at my parents' house."

Funny how every time you're confronted by authority, any anarchistic thoughts you had previously entertained, vanished, and the submissive tone that dominated your childhood years, pushes its way forwards, overcoming you in a single gesture.

Nails looked at me, shook his head, looked at my passport again and frowned.

"British, eh?"

"Yes sir."

"Could you pull up next to Passport Control, and present your documents at the front desk please?"

Now I was worried. About what, I wasn't sure, it could have been anything. I'd been cut off from the world for three months, and for all I knew, Britain and Canada could be at war. We pulled up outside and I climbed out, passport in one hand, cigarette in the other. Flicking the butt on the

116

floor, I ground it out and walked towards the entrance. Maybe they had to wait until you actually crossed the border before they could charge you with smuggling. Standing behind the desk was the cop from the Village People. I looked again to see if I'd been mistaken. I wasn't. He was a dead ringer for the disco policeman. If he broke out the rubber gloves, only one of us was going to have any fun. And it wouldn't be me.

"I was told by the chap at Border Control that I had to come here and show you my passport."

"Ah yes sir. British are you? Do you want your passport stamped?"

"Excuse me?"

"Do you want your passport stamped with a Canadian entry visa? A little souvenir of you visit."

A stamp? I'd shit myself over a stamp? Stamp away my disco liege, stamp away. And while you're at it, show me some of those funky moves that brightened up Top of the Pops.

"Uh, yes please."

He stamped once, he stamped twice and that was that. It was all over.

"There you are sir. Mind how you go, eh?"

What was it with the "Ehs"? Had everyone been taken over by the Pod People and were they communicating with each other in some dastardly alien code? I wasn't about to find out and made for the exit as fast as my trembling legs could carry me, and the Olympic opening ceremony. Doug had kept the engine running in case he needed to make a quick getaway.

"They bust you?"

"No man, we're clear. Let's go."

The Special Olympics ran their course, and in a close series of events, Britain came second, falling during the vodka relay, our failure being put down to a lack of preparation. Always be prepared because even the authorities like to bend the rules and play you for a sucker, reeling you in to fry in your own guilt while giggling all the way to the bank. Sometimes the joke's on you and like it or not, and even if you don't get it, you've got to laugh. After all, where would we be without laughter?

120

20

Popping The Freehand Cherry

From day one I observed the significance of ritual. The lives that revolved around and depended upon set events at certain times, regular as clockwork; we set our watches by the celebrations that litter the Roman calendar. Family gatherings became the antithesis of my existence, fat aunts and uncles getting drunk, pinching cheeks and telling all and sundry about how good it was in the old days. The ones that didn't end in punch ups, finished with empty promises to get together more often, when everyone involved knew it was merely a coping mechanism, a way to deal with the twenty hours a year they already had to spend in each other's loathsome company. If it wasn't family, it was mythical figures in bullshit scenario's, Santa Claus, The Easter Bunny, The Tooth Fairy, a legendary foursome who would have made the ultimate tag team, ready to take on anyone if it wasn't for the laughable circumstances in which they found themselves. I often wondered what The Easter Bunny made of his role as he prepared himself to paint the town red on a Saturday night, frantically trying to force his ears under a baseball cap.

"Stay down, stay the fuck down. Please stay

down and don't let anyone see me..."

Forget the ears buddy; they're the least of your problems. It's the teeth and that carrot that you should be worrying about.

Pissed off didn't even come close to where I was at. I'd had a bellyful of inbred idiots and quasi-religious fantasies and needed a change, a break from the norm, a ritual I could call my own. The so-called backward nations still believed in tribal scarring to commemorate a young man's coming of age and bodily decoration to stress individuality, and this seemed a much better bet than the suit and tie gateway to a pension plan. I set off to search for the nearest tattoo artist, my body ready to become a shrine to the colour of the needle.

The white walls of the studio were filled with designs to suit every mood, the brilliance of the background shining between the spaces that separated each pattern. It was no different to a doctor's waiting room, save for the fact that the artwork was far superior and receptionists don't usually have beards! In a weird kind of way it was relaxing; the aura of familiarity put my nagging doubts at ease and revived my determination. I chose my colours and waited. Patiently, quietly, laughing nervously as the other customers cracked fear inspired one liners. The door opened and I was ushered in, the technicalities of placement and size were worked out in the blink of an eye and I sat down eager to take my medicine. As soon as the gun started, the noise it made immediately transported my mind into the dentist's chair and my in-built terror kicked in without warning.

My fear was born from experience and the fact that my dentist's hands shook, that he regularly sported three days' worth of stubble and almost always smelled of cheap gin. Eccentricity and alcoholism are part and parcel of the job if you're an actor, but not if you're a surgeon. Give me a fucking break; I'd rather have had a fucking muppet chop my gums than an old soak on a semi-permanent bender who was prone to blackouts. Cowardice presented me with a new set of options. I could save face and trust in a stranger or make like a tree and leave. If only I'd had the heart that the Lion was desperately searching for in Oz, I would have excused myself then and there and never looked back. The needle entered my skin and lights started to flash in front of my eyes. It stung. No, it hurt like hell, but it wasn't unpleasant. It was the kind of pain you could get attached too and derive pleasure from if given enough time. I thought about the sadomasochistic movement and sexual deviants, and it finally began to dawn on me that maybe it wouldn't be so bad to wear a leather all in one and be beaten by a Russian woman called Olga. Then again, there were better things to do on quiet evenings, like cooking your balls in boiling fat. I chain smoked and made pleasant conversation with the torture king of the West Side. I had to keep him on my side and didn't even want to think about annoying him in case he transformed my tasteless design into something far more tragic.

"Nice weather we're having."

"If you say so champ. Now relax, it's time for the really painful bit. This is going to hurt…"

How time flies when you're having fun. The outline was finished; my creation was slowly coming to life, pulsing weakly as it bled. Igor it lives, my hunchbacked little worm, it lives. Taking shape as the colour was added, my familiar began to breathe, and I knew how it must have felt to be a father, holding his newborn baby for the first time. It was a masterpiece, adding to my body, providing strength and power, subtracting nothing, giving all. There was a new boy in town, his trade as old as the tribes that had bred humanity.

"Lovies, darlings, the ambience of the piece gives it a durable yet fragile, built to last air of all the punk rock yesterdays and spaces between the moments lost to us all."

Limping away, I started to feel as though I had taken the primary steps on the road to completion, stumbling though they may have been, I'd taken them. My right of adulthood complete, I wore my name tag with pride.

"Hi, my name is Tim. My interests are fucking, fighting and rocking out. I'd like to see the world burn in thermo-nuclear destruction. Give the roaches a chance."

Have we come so far that we've forgotten who we really are? Finding ourselves with nowhere to turn, shaped by festivals whose meanings are long submerged and buried by the wheels of progress, a nomadic monstrosity with a one-way ticket.

Roots? You've got to find your own and hold on tight, because no matter what else they can do, no one can take them from you. Happiness and belonging are just words that we're eternally doomed to chase.

21

Opportunity Knocks And
The Keystone Cops

What is it about me? Have I really got one of those faces? The visages that stare out at you from wanted posters, the eyes boring into the very core of your being while politely whispering "You fuck with me and I'll kill you. Then I'll kill you again and again until you can't be anymore dead. And then I'll kill you some more."

You know the type, the kind of guy you could take home to meet your family and share apple pie with, not the sort of chap who takes sweets from babies and chases old ladies, naked, through city streets on a hot afternoon. Personally, I've never done any of these things, appealing as they may be. Except for the apple pie thing. I did do that and it was one of the most terrifying experiences of my life. There's nothing special about me, you wouldn't recognise me on a crowded street. Unless you wore a blue uniform and had sworn to uphold the law in any way that you saw fit to interpret it.

Like any young male I felt it only right to test the boundaries of the world I grew up in. Experimentation with alcohol caused me to push a little too hard at times and led to me spending the odd night at Her Majesty's expense in a cramped six by six hotel room. The drill was always the same; sleep off the binge and contemplate the consequences of your actions. A slapped wrist followed by a "righteous" display of authority that culminated in breakfast, a free ride home and your family repeatedly asking why they had to be burdened by this black sheep. What had other parents done that they hadn't? Why them? Because I was a master criminal, wheeling and dealing, ducking and diving, stealing from the rich and giving to the poor? Or was it that I was another easy target for frustrated coppers with nothing better to do? They are who they are, and you came to expect the occasional "tug" by the forces of law and order. If you didn't get one, you'd start to worry and feel that you had to turn yourself in wildly confessing to any crime that came to mind. You could be fucked with at any time, for any reason in order to create a healthy respect for the law. All it really does is make you afraid and wonder what they're capable of. Behind every badge lurked a Cro-Magnon with an attitude problem, maladjusted and twisted by the same system that they'd sworn to protect.

It had been a couple of years since my last "pull", and I'd assumed quite naturally that me and the police no longer had anything in common and thus nothing to "talk" about and that I'd never have to share tea and biscuits with Sergeant Bastard again. Being a Friday night, I'd had a few drinks and decided to finish the evening with a game of Supernova. Supernova for those not familiar with the rules, involves climbing streetlights in a vain attempt to extinguish them. It had, never been done. Until this particular Friday. Poggles, one of my companions in inebriation, had despite the laws of gravity, managed to slither to the top and with a single blow, pop, bring on the darkness. However, what goes up, must come down, and down he came in a spectacular belly flop that crushed me underneath the descending champion – a make believe jury of impartial judges awarding him full marks for finesse and precision. Youthful high spirits satisfied, we proceeded on our merry way. Poggles, having somehow split his hand open when he turned out the light and initiated me in the Way Of the Warrior, left me to make my own way home covered in bloody palm prints.

Two hundred yards away from the sweet oblivion of sleep, my turn had come once more. Contestant number one, come on down and enjoy a magical mystery tour in the back of a Paddy Wagon.

"What am I supposed to have done?"

"Shut the fuck up!"

"Where are we going?"

"Shut the fuck up!"

Images of Rodney King flashed before my eyes. Beaten to a pulp and sodomised by a rubber truncheon in some far flung backwater. Bollocks. They'd seen the Supernova finals and having teased me with freedom, snatched it away at the last minute. Or so I thought as I was marched out of the van and into the station without a word of explanation.

"Sit there and shut up. Someone will deal with you in a minute."

It was going to be the rubber hoses then. It may well have been a frame up, but I was already blubbering like a new born baby and was ready to crack and sing like a pet canary.

A scuffer walked in, looked at me, handed me a plastic beaker half full of lukewarm tea, turned and walked out. Alone, my imagination ran riot. I pictured the door bursting open every thirty seconds, trigger-happy police running in, screaming and then doing a little quick step on my face. A suit covered in arrows with a ball and chain around my ankle, singing Old Man River as I broke rocks in the hot sun was the only image of my immediate future that I could drag from my terrified subconscious. I drank, all the while thinking about what remained of my short, short life. The tea tasted like piss, or what I thought piss would probably taste like – I prayed that I'd make it out and one day would be thirsty enough to find out if I was right while chained up in a sordid sex dungeon. An hour passed with no sign of life. This time I was really in it, I was floating up shit creek in a leaking canoe without a paddle. Bladder and bowel control on the verge of giving up, I prepared to accept twenty-five to life as calmly as possible. They must have heard me halfway around the globe as the tears flowed. This was it. The door opened.

"Okay, you can go now."

I trotted my little curly tail out of there in double quick time, whelping, all the way home to mummy. If they weren't laughing, I was the King of Spain. Once again, the police had fucked with me and there wasn't a damn thing I could about it, I just assumed the position and behaved myself and let their nasty medicine make me all better. Boredom does strange things to a person – especially those in a position of power. Prevention becomes the cure, the disease becomes secondary to the symptoms and the diagnosis is always swept under the rug. So, on those long, cold lonely nights when you're bored and wishing on a star that something would happen, just remember that you're never too old for tea and biscuits and there's always someone, somewhere who wants to talk to you.

22

Calling In Sick

Adjusting the rear view mirror, I blinked, hoping that I'd been wrong. I hadn't. The fifth horseman of the apocalypse drew closer, flames surrounding his black metallic chariot as it tore down on me. Escape was impossible. Thunder echoed, lighting crashed, he sped past and winked at me. I'd been flat busted and it was all because of a punk rock show. Bet on a sure thing and you know it'll come in last, lame and on its way to the glue factory. Usually I'd have turned around, engulfed in self-pity getting ready to study the situations vacant section of the local rag. But this was no ordinary show. It was NOFX and tomorrow was another day. Fat Mike would provide the answers that granted me immunity from prosecution, coming up with a last minute solution that would prove beyond any reasonable doubt that I was an inno-cent man, falsely accused and held in chains. Besides the worst thing that could happen was that I'd get fired. And I'd been there, done that and bought the postcard more times than I could recall. No big deal.

I'd been working as a laboratory technician for a geological firm for three months, and had dis-covered that my contract was open to any number of interpretations. All of which depended on the individual's point of view and my manager reserved the right to change anything at any time without prior consultation. Not that the job was exacting in any way, it wasn't. It basically involved putting mud into various size pots and weighing it. The reason for this is still eludes me, but if somebody wanted to pay me for playing in the dirt, who was I to complain? It's simple logic like this that always leaves me with egg on my face, bitching to no one in particular and makes me my own worst enemy.

My first day had been spent learning all there was to know about the job. I could wash mud, pack mud, hammer mud and make mud sit up and beg by the end of it. I was a mud professional in every sense of the word. I hadn't even considered where the mud came from, it was there, neatly wrapped in bags tied up with a variety of coloured bows. It was easy, I'd found my free ride, grabbed a bucket and spade and dived right in. It must be a male thing, some deeply buried childhood issue that reared its scruffy head whenever the chance to be a kid again arose that let you forget about things like pay, hours and working conditions by assuming that the world is a wonder-filled cavern and everyone is your friend. Common sense became alien when the chance to get covered from head to toe in foul smelling shit and finish your playtime with a bag of sweets presented itself. And it really was sort of fun. Right up until I found out where my new toys had come from.

On the third day I was sent out to bring in what my considerate boss lovingly called samples. Samples? I puzzled over this for a while and decided that it was a corporate term for dirt, and dutifully carried out my task. The danger signs had all been there, I'd just chosen to ignore them, not even thinking about what I was carrying. This charade continued for about six weeks until the boredom level of my chosen trade forced me to sit up and take stock of my new life. I started to read the packaging. Caution, contaminated samples. Contaminated? Was there too much sand? Was the gravel level too high? Curiosity killed the cat, and I took the bait.

"So, when they say contaminated, what exactly does that mean?"

"Oh, the usual."

Well, that's all right then if it's only the usual, there can't be anything to worry about.

"What do you mean, the usual?"

"You know, heavy metals, carcinogens and industrial waste."

I swallowed my tongue, my lips turned black, and I had to count backward from one hundred to stop myself passing out. When I reached fifteen I was ready to continue.

"Isn't that a little dangerous?"

"Of course it is. What did you think you were being paid for?"

I sort of thought that I was being paid to make sandcastles and mud pies. Silly me.

"I guess they wouldn't put us in any danger, and our safety has got to be important, right?"

I could hear the pause in my voice.

"Sure, but the boss spent the safety budget and the money for new extractor fans and face masks on a new extension for his house."

My easy gig suddenly seemed like a death sentence, and I thought about lying in a hospital bed with my eyes bulging from their sockets, caught in the final stages of radiation sickness. If I was going to get cancer it was going to be on my terms, sharing an iron lung with the Marlboro man, watching Lee Van Cleef and humming the theme to Rawhide. The closest I wanted to get to heavy metals was frantically riffing away on an air guitar to old Black Sabbath records.

I remembered the words of Karl Marx and decided to lead a worker's revolution. Fanatics were needed and all I had to help further my cause were a mummy's boy, a pervert and a bloke whose sole topic of conversation was rugby. Rome wasn't built in a day, and carefully I put my every waking effort into the pursuit of liberty and justice for all. Adopting my best phoney accent, I put a handkerchief over the telephone receiver and dialled the saviours of the blue collar man – the Health and Safety department of the local council.

In hushed tones I informed them of the numerous complaints I'd gathered, and waited for them to storm the company, machine guns spitting lead retribution, stun grenades going off, whilst they blocked every exit and avenue of evasion. They'd free the working hostages and try Herr Commandant under article 57 of the Geneva convention and imprison him for industrial criminality and his flagrant abuse of his employees' human rights. It was futile gesture of a dying man, as the posse never arrived. I hunkered down and gave up hope and started to realise that it was going to be a long winter.

I consulted all the wise men that frequented the drinking establishments in the area. The mutual agreement was that I had to get myself fired. Easy, I'd just be the antagonistic prick that every punker knew deep down inside that he or she could be. But no matter how many buttons I pushed, nothing ever worked. I had dug my own grave in the mud that it had been so much fun to play in. I took all kinds of liberties, insubordination, turning up late and repeatedly calling in sick. It was during one of my fun filled periods of pretend nausea that the horseman placed his icy finger of authority upon my shoulder.

My number up, I shuffled into his office the next morning, eyes held open by matchsticks, hangover bouncing around in my skull, ready to demand the maximum sentence. Fuck leniency, give me what I've got coming. He didn't even look up.

"You're fired, get your stuff and go."

"Right ho!"

If he expected me to plead with him, he had the wrong guy. See you later alligator. Unemployment, poverty and long mornings spent in bed were a luxury that I revelled in for the next three months. If a situation seems too good to be true, that's because it almost certainly is and if you draw the short straw then you can't fix the dam. But you know what they say, if it isn't broken, don't fix it. Mike, I can't thank you enough.

23

Until The Stars Burn Out

It was summer, I remember that much. One of those days when you can smell the static in the air and the moisture hangs from your clothes. Ann, her name was Ann. Her eyes reflected a picture of sympathy, her touch was electricity, raw, flowing, a wave from the centre of her soul that overwhelmed, disabled and disarmed its victims. Entangled in her net, drawn closer, her desire charged my cage. I was blinded, my cataracts put in place while strapped to a laboratory slab, and a million wires discharged current, polluting my slowly convulsing body. She stood in the distance, a vague shape in the ebony collage, toying with the switch, judging each single reaction as my "on" position was found, lost, and then found again. Meat, infested by its own virulence, crimson as it oxidised, that's all any of us were, meat to experiment with and sculpt. All positions were acceptable and art was the forum that vanquished pain. The hunger was insatiable, the more I ate, the more I needed, gorged and obese, unaware that I was slowly dying. My lifeforce draining away, leaving an emaciated shell, limbs drying in the desiccated atmosphere that was generated by my own lust.

Pleading, she gazed at me, every pupillary response asking me how I could abandon paradise, how I could walk away from Eden. Just as Cain had struck down Abel, driven by remorse I turned my back, an impossible action, the last impulse of a drowning man. Drowning in pride and the raging waters that drove the turbines of my self-determination. Reactions muted by the uncontrollable power that slammed into and distorted their super structure, crushing my free will, the pressure threatening implosion. Move, move, got to go fucker, forward, upward, ever onward, it's a race against time and the sands are already in motion. Glancing back, the pleas had turned to fury and my true adversary had shown herself. Her hands were soaked by blood, staining her pale skin, pulling her back into the mire of a long forgotten past, assuming a reserved seat on a masochistic steed bound for damnation, the fast track to understanding. Forgiveness is the first step to realisation and in the eyes of my fellow men I was a sinner. But even a sinner has the right to suffer and punish those who have stood against him, serving vengeance in the multitude of forms that eventually became another course on the menu. For five years I had struggled against one another, gaining an inch only to give a mile, hostilities ended by a series of ceasefires and conference table agreements that were ultimately doomed to fail. I wanted it. I needed it. I had to have the pain, the anguish and the mistrust that made me whole. Without them I was nothing, a crumbling ruin in a garden of stone, whose ambitious vegetation dragged me down, as the bowels of the earth opened and waited to greet another of the lost children. Welcome home, come on in, put your feet up, stay a while. If I listened carefully, I could hear the faint call of elevator music that was piped into my non-stop ride to damnation.

Love. The word left me choking on feathers, a four letter excuse to wear flared pants, garishly coloured caftans and thrift store beads. It was a sickness that spread like wildfire, devouring even the staunchest non-believers, sealing them in a chrysalis, preparing for the transformation that would leave the everyday world behind. This wasn't love, it was emotion stripped to its elemental components, barbaric lust that drew the beast from the man, tearing away logic and grinding reason to powder. No sense, no feeling just an urge to fuck, fuck and fuck some more. Over and over and over, I couldn't have stopped if I'd wanted to.

Who needed sleep? It was a burden that I'd shed, that I'd traded for the feeling that swells your testicles to the size of coconuts and reduces motor function to a primitive growl. How many times had I stared at her smiling face? Listened to her reassurances that I was the only one, knowing full well that I was merely another number, another way to spend a boring afternoon? Between the hours of one and five you'll get your kicks between the sheets, feel the heat and join with it. Pull my strings as I delicately manipulate yours, each caress sliding into the next, escaping unnoticed, as candy coated secrets are exchanged. Meaning everything at that crucial moment, vaguely recalling vows as it fades, filtering through the cold night air. It had been too long and there'd been too many times.

I watched her wipe the tears from her face, wanting to hold her and smell her perfume, lose myself in her arms as the world turned. Two wrongs don't make a right, if I'd returned on my knees and begged for release, things would be the way they'd always been. I'd be safe in the continuity of finishing what I'd started. It would be simple, the easiest test, multiple choices for the emotionally subnormal that would let me reach out and touch someone. I watched her as she chose and circled her next target, carefully avoiding the obstacles as she moved in for the kill. Flicking her hair back, she smiled and touched his arm. His pupils dilated as her charge hit him, reeling, he stared into forever and in that moment became as lost as I had been. The circle broken, I greeted the new dawn and shared an old joke with it, noting the possibilities as they were pointed out, spiralling and interlocking. It was new day and I was a new man. Refurbished and ready for the next buyer. Caveat emptor, my friend, caveat emptor.

24

Mummy, What Does God Look Like?

Attention worshippers, as of Easter Sunday in this the year of our lord, two thousand and nine, homosexuality is a valid expression of affection between two consenting adults. All citizens are advised to read the King James Bible in reference to the tale of Adam and Eve. According to our research, they had two sons, Cain and Abel which created a love triangle. Cain grew jealous of Abel's desire for the woman known as Eve, and smote him a mighty blow which resulted in a mortal head injury.

Although there is no physical evidence of a relationship between the two brothers, Adam was Eve's main squeeze, and as she couldn't be in two places at once, this would contravene all the known laws of physics which all citizens have been instructed to hold in the highest regard. Therefore, it is the finding of this elected body that while their parents were consumed with lust, Cain and Abel did enter into a relationship of the homosexual variety, buggering the living daylights out of each other at every available opportunity. Oral pleasure and mutual hand relief are also thought to have played a major role in the friendship as both men rejoiced in the sins of the flesh.

However, Cain was not enough for Abel and he looked to his mother to satisfy his needs. Upon seeing this Cain was quick to anger and argued with his brother regarding his whereabouts on the night in question. Once again, without concrete proof we cannot be sure what the argument was about, but Abel is thought to have told Cain that he was popping to the Garden of Eden to pick some of the forbidden fruit in order to celebrate their newly discovered state of grace. Learning the truth, Cain refused to prepare the said fruit and during a temporary loss of control, struck Abel with the apple peeler. Seeing what he had done, Cain fled, living out the rest of his days in a sordid masturbatory fantasy fuelled by his memories of the days and nights he spent with his brother. So, I beseech you brothers and sisters, get fucking for the second coming is nigh and the juices shall flow as they have never flowed before. And on your way out, slip a little something in the poor box. All donations are gratefully received.

25

Are We Having Fun Yet?

You never forget the first time. It has no place in the history books, there'll be no statue erected to it to remind those who follow, and it becomes another open and shut case that's solved in the celestial wink of an eye. Another fragmented moment that's fondly recalled and rarely talked about by the wide eyed innocents too intent on running to the fold of the jaded and experienced to consider where their chosen path is taking them before they end up cynical to the last, bent out of shape and crucified to the cross of exhibition. Adrenaline takes over and bridges the rift between heaven and hell and propels mere mortals through the gates of purgatory while enforcing the belief that all things are possible. Shedding the burden of virginity is never as easy as it's made out to be as you clutch in vain at any straw offered and cross the finishing line while the smoke from the starter's pistol still hangs in the air.

Show time. Walk it like you talk it. To them it was simply another Sunday, a brief respite from family life, but to us, it was a new beginning. We were selling the work of fevered minds that rebelled against anything and everything we could. If they could put it up, we would tear it down. It was a matter of principle and even if we were nothing else, we'd always been men of principle

I was ready to abandon ship, fuck all the women and children, I wanted to drift off the edge of the world, floating aimlessly away while dwelling on what might have been. Everyone had turned up and started to argue about what we should play and the order in which the set should be delivered. I didn't care. They were all going to be played, one was as good as another, so what did it matter? It wasn't a science fair and we weren't racing white mice through a maze. Our job was to shake the crowd until their teeth rattled and they fled for the border, clutching their heads as their ears bled. Pixie looked at me and grinned in sheer terror. We formulated a plan. One in which we'd pool what-ever money we had, head home, get blind drunk and leave the others to explain our mysterious disappearance. We'd fade into the background, get sucked into the Bermuda Triangle and hand jive all the way to the bottom. While Pixie was panicking, I felt nauseous, the kind of sickness you get as a child when you've stayed on the roundabout for too long or rolled too far down the hill. Refusing to pass, the nausea continually poked me in the stomach to remind me who was really in control in case I somehow forgot as my mind flip-flopped between certainty and fear, the flopping gradually ensuring that the latter remained firmly in control.

"Men, we stand on the verge of a great victory. What we do in the next hour will determine the course of our lives as we know them. Some of us might not make it through, and that is unfortunate. But know this, you give everything for the struggle so that others might taste the spoils of war, and join us as we shout and scream at the trap in which we are ensnared. Go out and make me proud. Victory or death!"

As speeches go, it was pretty great. I'd spent an hour working on it and was fully prepared to deliver it. That extra little push we needed to jump off the ledge. I stood, assumed my best bravado driven stance and started waving my arms around, practising. I must have looked almost as stupid as I felt.

"Come quick, there's a punker spazzing out. I think he's been eating the blue toilet blocks."

Knowing that we'd stand or fall on the strength of this performance, each of us retreated into our own space before coming together as a whole. Darren had brought half of Jamaica's favourite annual crop with him and started to smoke like it was going out of fashion. If he'd been any more relaxed he'd have been horizontal. Ian sat in the yoga position on the toilet, chanting the same sentence over and over –

"Don't let us suck, don't let us suck".

Chug crouched in the corner, a big dumb smile plastered on his face. He usually had trouble remembering not to drag his knuckles on the ground, but this time stupidity seemed to favour the fortunate as he picked his nose, examined what he'd removed and put it in his mouth, relishing the taste. Being able to think could be regarded as a curse, and it was a burden that Chug had never had to carry. He was a wind-up monkey without a care in the world and two forward gears. Pixie frantically played each song, pushing every chord sequence further into his subconscious. And while my bandmates individually dealt with our collective fate, I just rocked back and forth, reciting lyrics and mumbling "I will not forget, I will not forget".

The lights dimmed, I closed my eyes, took a deep breath and leapt into space. The first song hurtled past. They were applauding. For us. They actually liked it. Quickly as it had appeared, the sickness vanished, replaced by a strange feeling of euphoria. Fuck, this was better than sex, the rush was insanely powerful and was almost like mainlining adrenaline, providing an instantaneous hit. That was it, lock, stock and barrel, I was gone and there was no coming back. The hecklers started.

"You suck!"

A call demanded an answer and I was more than happy to provide one

"And so does your mum."

With that small glitch in the programme over, the rest of the show finished far too quickly...I didn't want to leave, I couldn't leave. I'd tasted heaven and found a reason for my otherwise pointless existence. This was what I was born to do. It all made sense, the direction I'd been pushed in, waiting quietly for a sign. I rolled up my sleeves, fell to my knees and begged for more.

Since that first time, I've played more shows than I care to think about and the feeling never changes. The theme varies every now and then, but it's all worth it and for those five minutes I'd hand over everybody's balls on a silver platter. Don't take my word for it, try it yourself. It could be the best meal you'll ever have.

156

26

There's A Right Way, And This Is The Wrong Way

When you're running on a tight budget, each and every penny has to be accounted for and swift mental calculations calculated on a make believe abacus. Cutting corners, dispensing with middle men and snatching victory from the jaws of defeat become accepted practices. Fabricating something from nothing with a little cunning is an art form, acquired over time by watching others fall flat on their faces. It was our turn to sink or swim, if we flew too close to the sun, we'd plunge to a watery grave and spend eternity sleeping with the fishes. Being the astute businessmen and clever punk rockers that we were and with our allegiance to the "do it yourself" ethic firmly in place, we'd found the venue to commit our material to tape, selling ourselves without selling out. Rank outsiders, no longer a name on an ageing flyer, people would travel from far distant shores to see us after hearing our fury, transplanted to mass produced cassettes. Or so we thought. Enthusiasm and naiveté are no substitutes for wisdom and patience.

To this day, recording leaves a bad taste in my mouth, one that's stale and flavourless, diluted by the hands of the blind and uneducated. Hindsight has a habit of throwing stones at glasshouses, disturbing what should have been laid to rest, making you cringe as the bitterness floods back, in wave after endless wave. We'd seized the opportunity of a day's recording at a fraction of the normal price, laughing all the way to the bank, thinking that luck was working for, instead of laughing at, us for a change. That motherfucker saw us coming a mile away and pushed all the right buttons in exactly the right order. We were his for the taking and take us he did; all the way to the cleaners.

Expecting a sanctuary dedicated to the purity of noise, I got that all too familiar sinking feeling in my stomach as our convoy pulled up outside. I did a double take because maybe I'd been wrong, but the sign didn't lie and the writing was right there on the wall. Pontycymmer Working Men's Hall. The place were dreams went to slowly die, soaked in stale beer and bombarded by infinite tribute acts and near suicidal comedians. Rushed down a stairwell with only a torch to guide our way, my thoughts turned to Peter Cushing and Doug McClure, and dug in to prepare for the onslaught.

"Walk toward the light children, walk toward the light".

He beckoned us forward, proudly standing by his mixing desk that was a mess of tangled wires that looked ready to short out at any minute. The spirit of seventies metal was alive and well and completely filled the frame of our engineer. I half expected the Bee Gees to walk in behind him playing his theme song, inaudible over the noise his jewellery made as it rested on his chest hair that was exposed by his half open leather shirt. I didn't know whether to laugh or cry, but he was one of the bravest fuckers I'd ever met. Either that or he was clutching to some far fetched dream of super stardom that had long since abandoned him. Flicking his freshly permed hair over one shoulder, he swaggered toward us.

"Okay, guys, go and set up. I'll be in now to mike you."

No matter how hard we tried, none of us could ever imitate his walk properly; we just couldn't get it right. His glide was smoother than what any of the go-go dancers I'd seen pull off impossible moves while accompanied by Motown's finest on late night Soul Train repeats could ever have come up with.

The walls were covered with various calendars celebrating the female's role in the workplace, bikini clad vixens clutched tyres and sprawled over engines demonstrating the applications of the torque wrench. Under these lay the mattresses which doubled as sound proofing and if you looked at them for too long, the after hours stains that our engineer had left on them burned their way into your memory. Sex machine glided in, his arms filled with a variety of microphones. He was the master of Big Hair Farmland and at his crazy, crazy prices, everything had to go. If you wanted it, he had it. If he didn't have it, then you didn't need it.

Have you ever seen those old NASA films about preparing astronauts for space flight? Getting miked up was like that, by the time he'd finished we all were boxed into the corners of the room and began fighting over what little oxygen there was.

"This one goes here and that one goes there, and one up each of your rectums for good luck".

"So, who do you want to sound like?"

"What?"

"Who do you want to sound like? Which band?"

Brilliant. A fucking engineer who didn't know what kind of band we were. Here's a thought, take a little of The Jackson Five, a pinch of Duran Duran and top it all off with a sprinkling of U2. And then splice it according to taste.

"It's punk rock."

"Oh, you mean like The Sex Pistols?"

Yeah, that's right you fucking hairy monster. We want to sound like Malcolm's third rate boy band.

"Look just make it loud, lots of guitars, plenty of aggression and energy."

"Whatever you say, man."

Man? Wake up, it's not seventy-four anymore. Grand Funk have split, Lennon's dead and The Grateful Dead sold out a long time ago. Reality check for Mr Sex Machine, please hold the line, you've become untethered in time again.

"Ready when you are."

Chocks away, it was go time. The mistakes came thick and fast, each one forcing the aggression level up, the air grew thicker, the room hotter and body odour poisoned the oxygen we couldn't spare. After four hours none of us gave a flying fuck about anything. United by blood, we were compadres in crime.

"You want to hear what I got down?"

Yes, damn it, we did want to listen to the tape that was destined to collapse society from the outside in. Out of fifty-three recorded tracks, we could use six. Six. Have you heard the one about the hardcore band? You have? Well, here's a copy of their demo that couldn't punch its way out of a ripped paper bag. Flat? Our spirit level barely moved, its flaccid bubble permanently lingering in its perpetual comfort zone. The revolution would have to be postponed. I needed a shower. The whole experience had left me feeling dirty. Quality not quantity was the most expensive date I ever had and the only thing waiting at the end of it was a humiliating sense of misadventure. It's a wonderful life.

27

Mysterious Island

There are places on this earth that will never be charted or explored by man. Wonders beyond our wildest imagination fill these far away corners of the globe, and I know this to be true. Television told me so, and the cathode ray can't lie. It was made to be faithful until the failure of its silicone heart, its life span aided by the transplantation of micro circuitry. In the hands of a good surgeon and soldering iron, it can struggle on indefinitely, a lover, companion and advisor to each new generation, flourishing under the watchful eye of its neon glow. Escapism without forfeit, so many different fantasies to become part of, control achieved, plug in and feed.

Fleeing in vain across the endless sands, the demon bird of "Mysterious Island" was gaining ground, the possibility of escape decreasing with every step. The captain turned to meet the evolutionary throwback, one on one. With no rules laid down by The Marquis of Queensbury, they'd use whatever damn weaponry came to hand and only one of them would walk away.

I leaned forward in my chair, bracing myself for the imminent clash of the Titans, lovingly preserved on B grade celluloid. Daylight shattered the darkness and dragged me kicking and screaming back to reality. There'd be no epic battle for supremacy this day and no confrontation with Mother Nature and her servants of the night.

A child, no matter how young or old can always tell when something is wrong with or between its parents. Science comes up with an answer, genetic links, mental chains, empathy, in the world of nine to five these hypotheses mean jack shit and are about as clever as pissing in the wind.

The news I'd been waiting for, was about to be revealed. There were two possibilities and one truth, and acceptance is often the hardest game to play. Oh, you can smile, say its fine and choke on your own rage until your face turns blue and your fingers black. Doesn't mean you have to like it, but a thousand "fuck yous" won't alter the facts or persuade destiny to change its mind. Things are the way they are and you can't turn back the hands of time. Acceptance. I'd spent the morning flipping a coin, muttering "If it's heads everything will be fine, no problem".

It was a desperate attempt to change fate that was doomed to fail. Karma kept mocking me each time I tried to reason with it.

My mother had been crying and although he was smiling, my father looked pale and drained. White? Shit, he was transparent, and I swear I could see the pattern of the wallpaper he was standing in front of. He'd been feeling like death warmed up for about a year, with all kinds of symptoms and each time he'd seen a doctor they'd been unable to find out what was wrong with him.

"Ladies and gentleman, this case provides science with one of its greatest challenges of the last millennium. So far we haven't been able to pinpoint the exact cause of distress and when we are faced with problems of this kind we reach into the magic hat and grab hold of the acclaimed White Rabbit. Alternatively, we close our eyes, spin around in a circle and take a wild guess. Bearing this in mind I prescribe Doctor Killemall's Marvellous Miracle Linctus and a course of leeches".

Fucking Quacks. Hey, come to medical school, pass a couple of exams and venture out to heal the masses. Don't worry, most of them are faking anyway and even if they're not, fuck it you've got a diploma and a career path to follow haven't you?

Eventually, like all good politicians, the medical world caved and agreed that they didn't have a clue and asked him if would he like to go for some "routine" tests. Does it hurt when I stick this needle in your eye? How about when I pass electricity through your scrotum? These "routine" tests included x-rays, which he'd gone for this morning, and from the look of sheer disbelief, I guessed that he'd had the results. Yeah, I was a regular Einstein, a certified genius without direction or focus.

No news is good news and the truth hurts. Sit down young man, we've got to talk. They were going to talk to me, not at me, which was always a sure fire recipe for disaster and usually meant that the figurative locomotive had jumped its tracks and was heading for a school full of disabled children. Who can help us now? When I snap my fingers you will wake up and have no memory of the preceding events.

"Pardon? What did you just say?"

"Weren't you listening?"

Of course I was listening, I'm always listening. I'm clever like that. They seek me here, they seek me there, like the chameleon I'll blend into the background listening to the conversations nobody wants me to hear. Then, when they're not ready, I'll rise, a phoenix from the ashes of deceit to crush the ineffectual and rule with a rod of iron, forged from the molten waste of nihilism and cynical mistrust.

"Yeah, I was, but it just kind of went over my head. I'm stupid, you should know you tell me often enough."

"I said your father has cancer."

"What? You're joking right?"

I looked over at him. He shook his head and smiled weakly.

"No, this is no joke."

"But it can be treated and everything will be okay. That's right isn't it Dad? They can treat it can't they?"

"It can be treated with hormone therapy and radio therapy, but there's no guarantee it can be cured."

Cancer. I tried imagining it, a black mass racing through his arteries consuming everything in its path, leaving minuscule bits of itself on every bone, in every tissue to continue the work of the Mother Ship. Devouring him from the inside, slowly eating away at his soul, reeling in its fatal fishing line, and as much as you thrash around and try to get away, you're caught on its hook being pulled inch by inch, closer to that final port of call.

I found myself thinking back to my first school and one of the parent-teacher evenings, which later became a tired excuse for teachers to rat on the kids, so that when their parents take them home, Mummy bear and Daddy bear can beat the shit out of little Baby bear and Goldilocks doesn't have a guilt trip. Like Pontius Pilot, they could stand back and wash their hands of the affair. I remember looking up at my father, thinking he could do anything.

"Dad, build me a time machine, I wanna go play with the dinosaurs."

"In a minute son."

"Dad, why doesn't everything just fly off the planet?"

"Well, son it's like this…"

But nothing lasts forever, and I made it to a point as I got older to disagree with everything he said and go against everything he stood for. If he said the sky was blue – "Fuck you, it's pink and it's always been pink". Occasionally he'd rise to the challenge, and battle would commence. More often than not though, he'd let it slide and walk away. Eventually it became so bad that the only time we could spend together was in front of the family guidance counsellor, television.

What could I say, what could I do?

"Sorry Dad for being such a prick, but, you know it's growing pains, and it is my job to fuck with you and everything you say."

"That's okay son, you'll be a parent one day and then you'll understand how it rips you apart and hurts you more than any disease could."

I cursed the medical profession. Were they just, as I had always suspected, completely self-obsessed and terminally stupid?

"And now I shall reveal that the murderer, was in fact Mr Body, with the revolver in the Study."

"Brilliant reasoning Doctor, but there is one small flaw in your theory."

"Oh, and what's that?"

"Mr Body was the victim."

I needed to blame somebody, I had to have someone to point the finger at. It's your fault and knowing that makes me feel better. Of course it does young man, now run along and play.

For the first time in my life, I looked at my father and realised what he was. He was just another average guy, one of the millions who made up the masses of humanity. He wouldn't run into a phone booth, change into some ridiculous costume, save the world and be back in time for dinner. He hadn't built a death ray and held the government to ransom. He was just a man who'd found out he had cancer, like so many others do each day. He was mortal and one day he'd die. Only that day would arrive a lot sooner than I ever imagined it would.

"Oh shit."

My father looked at me and smiled. He knew. I knew. I never did find out if the Captain killed the demon bird and escaped Mysterious Island. I never want to.

28

The Future's So Bright, I Gotta Wear A Lead Suit

Today I decided to stop worrying. What will be, will be. I lit a cigarette and watched low grade video tape of the bombing of Hiroshima and Nagasaki. You can never have enough megatons. Burn baby, burn.

I cracked open a beer and read about the ethnic cleansing that threatened to wipe out both sides of a civil war raging across Europe. Lambs to the slaughter, come on soldier boy show me what you've got.

I planned a vacation in Rio De Janeiro and booked a city tour with the death squads who cleaned up the homeless children and made the streets safe for the foreign investors who wouldn't pay the taxes their own countries charged. A pre-booked urban safari with a difference and a guilt free tour through the bullet riddled depths of suffering and sorrow.

I got hungry and settled on a tuna sandwich. God, it tastes so much better when they throw the dolphins through the mincer too.

I took all the paper I could find and started a fire. Screw the rainforests, chopping them down keeps people employed. Carbon Dioxide? Shit, if the levels rise, so does the temperature and I like it hot.

Where would we be without packaging? I collect it and think about the hardworking chemists and how their wonder drugs give animals a purpose and create mutant unborn babies.

We're spoilt for choice and don't realise how lucky we are. In fact, as I settled down to sleep, my mind was blank and I was troubled no more. Free at last, I dreamt of sunny days and fat pay cheques. I'm only human.

29

Marching To The Hippie Death Camp

Festival season was upon us again, the youth of the nation had dutifully packed their bags, kissed their parents goodbye and set off to be humiliated in foreign fields. Previous feats of endurance forgotten, they camped out in filth encrusted tents, denied the basic amenities, for a chance to see their favourite band play a pitifully short set, another whistle stop on a never ending tour. On paper, they're a great idea, all these bands on one bill, what more could you ask for you lucky devils? In reality the concept gets tarnished and loses its rosy glow. Surrounded by fools, a week's wages spent on a meal scraped off the hull of an oil tanker, you pray for a swift end before the heavens open and wash you away with the rest of the gutter slime. This time though, it was going to be different, instead of huddling together for warmth, we were booked to play. Admittedly, the Llantrisant Free Festival wasn't exactly the glorious centre of the festival circuit, but it was start and the first step on the journey to marble jacuzzis, Millennium Falcon shaped swimming pools and garages filled with muscle cars that were chauffeur driven by monkey butlers.

Passing through the gates, the security guy asked for our passes. Security? This was a new one for us, so we took the time to savour the moment.

"There you are my good man. I believe you'll find that we're due to play this afternoon."

"Uh, yeah, okay."

It was sort of life affirming to see that the entry requirements for security were the same as they were for bouncers. Have you got two fists, a bad attitude and a pathological need to hurt people smaller than you? You do? Then welcome to your career in people "management". We sat poised, ready to unleash our venom and all things considered, decided that exploration should be our prime directive for the day. Flashing our passes in the general direction of anyone who happened to glance our way, we assembled in front of the main stage. It was big enough to land a helicopter on.

Finally, I could establish my position as rock god, a thousand cigarette lighters would salute me as I choked and grunted my way through my punk rock manifesto. I could separate the crowd into two halves and have them do battle for my attention, their futures entirely dependent on my every word. As I dreamt of ridiculous futures, my colleagues shrugged and started to walk back to the cars. Puzzled, I followed and cornered Darren.

"What's going on? Aren't we playing?"

"Yeah, course we're playing, just not on this stage."

Where the fuck else was there? The place was desolate apart from the usual mobile slow acting poison outlets and a collection of pre World War Two marquees.

"What do you mean?"

"See that tent over there?"

He pointed to a canvas covered pyramid, the holes in it showing that it had fed generation after generation of moths.

"Yeah?"

Overwhelming caution caused my voice to rise a full octave. Look at me, I'm Sandra Dee.

"That's where we're playing."

I should have known. Why expect it to be easy? This was one of our shows, and problems and disappointment were our staple diet. It was time to chow down on another one of those miserable three course, happiness-free meals that always left you feeling empty and desolate.

I was handed a copy of the afternoon's running order and there we were, next on. Never having played a show during daylight hours was bound to be interesting. The safety blanket of inebriation and darkness had eluded us and we'd have to be tighter than OJ Simpson's defence lawyers. The "stage" was built from that night's firewood and a sudden gust of wind would have blown the marquee back over the fucking rainbow. I just wanted to get up and get the fucking thing over and done with as quickly as possible. I can smell a hippie at a hundred paces, and that stench only means one thing, trouble.

"Hey, how you doing?"

"Seen better days."

It's on the tip of your tongue, open your mouth and free your spirit monkey boy.

"Uh, huh, says we're on next."

Come on, give it to us, we're big boys now. We can take it.

"It's had to be changed because some bands have arrived late, and they've got a long way to travel."

Treat us like we're slow learners and do the decent thing. Explain.

"Anyway, what this means is that you guys will be playing after the next two bands, hope you don't mind?"

How nice of you to ask. Of course we don't mind, that would be just peachy. Would you like us all to bend over as well?

"Okay, no problem."

Obviously it didn't matter to the rest of the band, but I had places to go and people to see. One in particular. I thought about my father lying in a hospital bed, and how I'd promised to go and see him. Hell, I figured we'd finish and I could get there before visiting hours were over. So much for advance planning. I laughed and got back in my car and closed the fucking door behind me. Ian walked over and got in.

"You all right?"

"Yeah, I needed to be somewhere else today that's all."

A man's got to have some secrets; they help him to find purpose. This was too personal to let go of, it was the rage that was fuelling my fire. It was all I had.

"You sure?"

"I'll be fine, start unloading the gear; I'll be with you now."

Left to my own devices, I stewed in my anger, its heat nearly melting the plastic grip on the steering wheel. A million images flashed before my eyes, my life spread before me, a contoured landscape of mistakes and fuck ups fashioned by tectonic teen angst. They say a dying man gets to see it all and be at peace, but what about the living? Those of us left behind, when do we find peace?

The bands whose travel arrangements had torn up the day's schedule, the folk singers and African Jazz combo both played, dragging half hour sets into two hour free form improvisations. Groovy, if that's your pleasure sir. Condensation lined my windscreen, something had to give, my mind was spinning so fast it stood still.

"We're on."

I decided to use my rage, turn it into energy, explode on the stage and feel it crack beneath my feet. Two songs in, it hit me, a wave of nausea that spread from my toes to eyeballs and I had to stagger off before I passed out, dry heaving all the way. As soon as I breathed fresh air, I doubled over and fell to my knees. But the show must go on, so I crawled back in and finished the set, giving it everything that I had left. All over, drained, my strength gone, I prepared to return to my sanctuary. I had to stop the ride, I needed to get off.

"What's the fucking time?"

"Six-thirty mate."

It was too late, I'd missed it. Shit. I'd have to catch him later and hope he didn't mind. My father died two days later, and I never got to say goodbye. Never got to say so many things, but it was the choice I made. I could have left, I didn't and somehow I have to live with that decision. I never wanted to play that motherfucking show, but I did it anyway and that day I learned not to get jerked around and to follow things to the letter. If it's agreed, signed off on and ready to go then its black and white and if the corners start turning grey, walk away. Fuck them; just walk with your head held high. Sorry Dad.

30

Sweet Dreams And Brain Death

Every once in a while, I'll sample the hidden pleasures of public transport. Not often, just every now and then. Perched among the rubbish, stale wine and colourful graffiti – strategically placed to be in permanent view of old ladies and young children, I'll gaze out of the window and laugh uncontrollably, remembering a chance encounter that happened a lifetime and a half ago.

There was nothing extraordinary about the day, it was just a usual Saturday afternoon, the air hot and damp and all the usual freaks were taking their one way trip to oblivion except for one who was sitting at the front of the bus, scrutinising each and every passenger as they climbed on and off. Once in a while, he'd look up and meet my gaze, quickly averting his eyes, returning to the task in hand when he realised that I wasn't going to break. I couldn't help myself. He looked like Huggy Bear after a three day household cleaning product binge, and after an hour of diesel fumes and psychobabble, amusement wasn't easy to come by. My turn came and I jumped off, thankful for the feeling of concrete under my Converse and set off on my merry way. Something flashed in the corner of my eye, and I spun around in time to see

Huggy duck behind a wall. He wanted to play. Our game continued for the next twenty minutes, I turned and he hid. Turn, hide, turn, hide. Maybe he got bored, or maybe he couldn't help himself. I'll never know, but he had something to say and by Starsky and Hutch, was he going to say it.

"Excuse me."

I turned. This time he stood in front of me, eyes glazed, determined and unbowed.

"Yeah?"

"I saw you looking at me. You know who I am don't you?"

Ah, so this was the secret Masonic greeting that I'd heard so much about.

"You know who I am don't you?"

Don't look, don't look. Too late. At some point earlier in the day, he'd pissed himself and the resultant dark stain became the focus of my attention.

"I haven't got a clue mate. Fuck off and leave me alone?"

Of course, I didn't want him to go. I had to know who he was. I just couldn't think of anything else to say.

"You know that I'm a secret agent sent to expose communist sympathisers."

He sure had the right disguise. The wino pimp. Perfect for all occasions. Who would suspect him?

"You fucking what?"

This didn't phase him one little bit. After all he'd learned all about it in week six of secret service training. Face your enemy, no matter what. A bottle of Brasso helps. It steadies the nerves.

"I'm a secret agent sent to expose communist sympathisers, and I believe you are one of the plague, the scourge that I have been sent to eliminate. Who do you work for?"

I've always believed that an individual's political affiliations should be kept to oneself, but seeing as he'd fed me the opportunity to score a three point basket, I thought that I'd have some fun with him. After all, it was the weekend, it was party time.

"I am Agent XYZ, sent to infiltrate and bring down the capitalist edifice known as the Supermarket."

He considered this for a second, processed the details and exploded.

"Don't fuck with me. I've got friends who are authorised to take your life."

Shit, I was about to be terminated with extreme prejudice. Exposure to the Partridge Family can seriously damage your health. There was no backing down. He reached into his pocket. I thought he had a knife and figured that I was going to be stuck by a fucking lunatic with a James Bond fixation. As if it wasn't hot enough already. He pulled out a plastic toy camera and we locked horns.

"Our conversation has been recorded on this. You'll be hearing from my superiors. Be prepared for questioning at all times."

Returning his cereal freebie to his pocket, he turned and walked away, making sure that he wasn't followed. Go on, give the camera to Q, motherfucker. What the hell are you going to say?

"000, there's nothing on this micro-film."

"Bloody budget cuts. It's not like in the good old days, the Cold War. How do they expect a secret agent to do his job with substandard equipment?"

"000, it's an adjustment for us all, facing up to the economic realities of the new world."

I only met Ray, which I later discovered was his name, once more. By that time, he'd been held in a secure unit and had been released into the community, medicated to the gills under the care of a private nurse. His eyes were dead and his speech slow and slurred. His identity had been stripped away and his licence revoked.

Is the cure worse than the disease? If we have to sacrifice happiness for normality, then brother open the gates of the asylum, because I'm moving in and I'm never leaving. Stamp my ticket Ga-Ga Land and send me on a one way ride to oblivion and beyond. Give me freedom, or give me sanity.

31

One Bite Of The Poisoned Apple

So much to do and so little time. Another support at TJs and everything was running to plan, we were ready to go and kick the headliner's arses all the way back to the US of fucking A. The van was loaded full of sweaty punkers and their precious equipment, I pointed the nose toward the holy land, destination Mecca, warp factor ten. There was a schedule to keep, and no time to debate the finer points of quantum physics. We had to stay in fifth gear as long as possible, the clutch had been making strange noises that were about as healthy as the longest staying guest at the world's oldest leper colony. I imagined a cable composed of thousands of tiny threads and each time I pushed the clutch to the floor one of those threads snapped in a deliberate attempt to try and fuck us over. Uh uh, that wasn't going to happen. Even if I had to get out and push, the god's cursed van was going to get us there whether it wanted too or not. I wish I could say it was a pleasant journey that was made shorter by witty conversation, intellectual discussion and lively sing-a-longs, but apart from the odd grunt we were all too focused on the task in hand to pay any meaningful attention to each other. We just wanted to play the set, try not to look too bad, watch the other bands grind us into dust and then sneak away with our shit eating grins firmly in place.

We arrived and in the middle of my head a flat, monotone voice began to drone

"This is your captain speaking, would all passengers leave the vehicle in an orderly fashion, making sure that they don't leave behind any items of luggage."

Sound checks are the worst part of a show. They sap the spontaneity of a set and it's made even worse when you've got to wait for what seems an eternity before you can crank up and rock out. We waited. The headliners took the stage and checked every item of equipment they had ten times over, catering for every eventuality and possible disaster, leaving nothing to chance. Our turn came, and we let rip. I've never seen a sound man smile and have often wondered if it was a prerequisite of the job. Sound man wanted, must be happy to dwell in perpetual misery. Five minutes later we were sat heads in hands awaiting the certainty of our impending doom. It was my turn to set up our fabulous merchandising – one shirt available in two different colours. We liked to spoil our "meagre at best audience" for choice. I looked up at the headliner's display and shook my head. There was a shirt for each day of the week in every colour. I had a vision of a guy on their bus taking

orders and making shirts to individual specifica-
tions. David faced Goliath, stuck both shirts on the
wall, knowing full well that stories changed to suit
situations and we'd sell nothing that evening. The
homeless man watching the rich dine in the
splendour of the warm restaurant, no slice of pie
for the underdog. Deciding that this game of merchandising soldiers could go fuck itself, we figured that we'd exchange horror stories of one
man and his dog shows with the headliners
instead. Having crossed paths with them before, I
knew they were pleasant chaps with no illusions
about the glamour of the road.

They were harder to track down than the lost
kingdom of Atlantis, and we returned to our
corner, planning the evening's assault with mili-
tary precision. The fashion victims filed in, eager
to watch their heroes chew on the bones of the
harshly picked bridging acts. The lot of the support band is a curious one. No one is there to see
you, but you might make a few friends along the
way. With this comforting thought in mind we
turned on, turned up and set sail. The sound of one
hand clapping filled the room as each number
ended and another began, while we clung rigidly
to our mantra "Play as fast as you can and it'll all
be over soon". I'd always figured that if someone
was paying to be entertained, then entertain them
I would and at full force I'd put on a show they'd

remember us for. Driven by demons and self-esteem issues, I'd explain the problems of the world through my chosen method, and my pupils would fall asleep in their beds dreaming of revolution and would rise the next day ready to create a better place for the children of tomorrow. We were monkeys in a cage and to keep our interest they'd throw us the odd peanut, nodding to each other as they compared notes. The only way to get through it was to keep thinking it was just another show, just another show and that maybe we'd escape with a shred of dignity. We finished up and left the headliners to heal the sick and bring justice to the unfortunate. Drained, the usual kids made their way toward our barren band chattels' table, asked the usual stupid shit that was exponentially exaggerated by their first taste of alcohol.

"My friend thinks you guys rock. What do you think?"

All things considered, the illusion of simplicity is exploited to its maximum potential. How the fuck do you answer a question like that?

"What does your name mean?"

It's an example of how the underclasses are made to suffer by the punishing acts of the rich. Because, you know, class war and all that.

He moved from one corner to the next, illuminated in blinding white light, telling anyone who would listen that we were fucking brilliant, the best thing he'd ever seen. One of the headliners was a convert. For a split second, fame and fortune beckoned, we could give our bosses the finger and bring punk rock to the masses. The split second dragged into forever in my imagination and its illusion was only shattered when I caught a whiff of the overwhelming scent of cheap whiskey on his breath and realised that he probably didn't know who he was and in the morning wouldn't have a fucking clue who we were. I knew though. We were just another warm up act.

How did the headliners do? Does it matter? They could have played like shit and performed the dance of the sugar plum fairy and the kids would have lapped it up and begged for more. I pulled the shirts off the wall and threw them in a box that was balanced precariously on top of our battered equipment that was waiting to be loaded up for another journey to Nowheresville. Faced with overwhelming odds all you can do is give it your best shot, knowing that your best is never good enough. Because if it wasn't any fun, nobody would do it, right?

I closed my eyes and jumped into the pit, arms and legs flailing in unison with the other puppets, pumped by the pulsating rhythm of punk rock. Right or wrong, we'd have our day in the sun, but it wouldn't be this day. Apparently, it isn't the cable in the clutch that you should worry about. It's the ratchet.

32

Hardcore Royalty

I swear they were brothers. Buffy and Flid the clown princes of hardcore, the punkest guys I ever met, were sitting across from me, debating the merits of boiled eggs and pizza. They could finish each other's sentences, elaborate on tall tales of high adventure and romance and tell you exactly what every band in the scene was doing. I studied them as the van lurched around blind bends, the flight case I was perched upon swaying in time with the ancient shock absorbers. Their Mohicans stood proudly to attention as they bartered, nose rings twitching as one thrust and the other parried. It was infectious and put all things in perspective, encouraging you to put two fingers up to everything that had ever pissed you off. You couldn't help yourself, two minutes in their company and the dark clouds began to lift, and problems were seen for what they really were, irritating, but of no real consequence. Man, they could have sold snow to polar bears and left the deal as kings.

Road trips become harder as you get older and the naiveté of youth slowly begins to disintegrate and feed the cynicism that results in the cancerous lethargy which has forced every single punk rock hero to choke on their own indignation. Every band has a book full of horror stories that they'll gladly share and if you hear enough of them, you'll end up working in an office too scared to face the harsh actuality that's always ready to greet any and all new friends. Opinions are like arseholes, everyone has one, but you only feel comfortable wiping your own. Clean too many and you'll become a lead weight, useless, discon- nected, as your mind separates from your body to protect itself from the terrible truth of its reality. The ambiguity digests the inner battle as it was waged and lost in some decrepit rehearsal room. Buffy saw it differently, telling you, eyes blazing, that there was no retreat, no surrender, you fought until you died. If you didn't, what was the point? There was no joy to be had in being a door- mat. Speak now or forever hold your peace. He had absolutely no truck with that going quietly into the night bullshit. Put your dukes up and stand your ground. No motherfucker was going to annex his soul in the name of democracy. He was a caped crusader on a mountain bike, campaigning for every last one of us to utilise the privilege that guaranteed us the right to dye our hair whatever damn colour we liked, and allowed us to spit on government policy. Come the revolution, he'd be standing over a battered road map, organising rebel troops while smoking a big, fat Cuban cigar.

Militant students would build shrines to his memory and wear shirts that displayed his mandate and grinning face that would serve as a clip around the ear for oppressive dictatorships everywhere.

Flid was the straight man who delighted in pointing out the inconsistencies that held society over a barrel. If the rules said he couldn't do something, he'd do it just to show you that it could be done and if you didn't like it, so fucking what? That was your problem. You get one attempt at life, one go at the hoopla stall, don't sit back and let it pass you by, there's no time for regrets. Retirement homes are filled with the wasted dreams of a thousand salad days, and rent control is never imposed on the elderly. Act now because tomorrow never comes, the carrot that's dangled in front of the donkey, an illusion of mediocrity perpetuated by parental advice and the achievement manuals that led would be stockbrokers and interior designers from support groups to the grave. For every lie there was a hundred truths and even though the books have been doctored by experts and the figures always seem to add up, there's always a decimal point in the wrong place. As a child, Flid had spoiled countless magic shows by pointing out how the tricks were done. Mirrors, wire and sleight of hand couldn't disguise hard facts. Was everyone stupid? It was there for them to see, hidden in plain sight beneath the half truths.

A show is a show, but with these two on your side, you could relax knowing that you'd have a good night, and nothing would piss on your parade. Effort was rewarded with praise and a well-deserved slap on the back. They were debt collectors for the little man, ready to slam the night away in any armpit club held together by spit and semen, inviting one and all to bring a bottle and join the party.

Whatever life ends up throwing at you, remember that you did what you could in a time of uncertainty and sleep easy knowing that you couldn't have done anymore or tried harder. And for every person that fucks you over, there's another who wants you to find your purpose and fulfil your potential. Step back, think about everything that you're told and don't be who they want you to be. Be Buffy. Be Flid. Be who you were supposed to be.

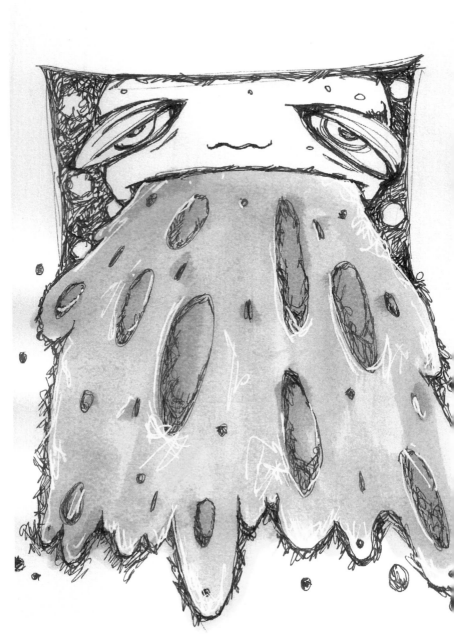

33

Debbie Did Dallas And All I Got Was This Lousy T-Shirt

Another show over, a small gap in the lives of the pitiful crowd filled, I sat down and reached for a beer. Some nights you pack up, your whole body rebelling and you know that if you don't crawl straight into bed you're just going to shut down and end up collapsing the middle of the street, lying there like a discarded rubbish sack. It's the other nights I live for. Wired, alive and at one with the universe, the lord of all you survey. This was one of those nights.

Steve, the guy who owned the pub we'd played in, had been cool with us, all of our drinks had been on the house and we'd made some door money as well. Which wasn't just unusual, it was a bone fide miracle. Most people who ask you to do shows carefully play a game of cat and mouse with the band, avoiding them at all costs and when cornered and asked about petrol money they come up with a list of twenty-three excuses about why they shouldn't, won't and can't pay you.

Steve only wanted someone to drink with, so I'd figured what the hell, I'd be his shoulder to cry on as long as I could dip my being into the fountain of inebriation. Goodbyes were said, the rest of the band exited stage left and left me to wallow in vodka. Bottle after bottle was finished while each of us desperately tried to imply that we were worse off than the next man. You think that's bad, you should try walking a mile in my shoes, you wouldn't last a day and all manner of other such cringeworthy, drunken sincerity and seven-eighths cut nonsense. Steve finally passed out with a smile on his face and no doubt dreamt of early retirement on a Caribbean island populated solely by ex-strippers who now worked for a co-operatively owned distillery.

That left three of us left. Little man, fat chump – I know, labels are for chain stores, but this guy was fucking big – and yours truly. The night was young and stimulation in short supply. We needed naked women and firewater, no preferential order, as long as we got them nothing else mattered. As soon as the Neanderthal part of our brains kicked in, the urge became greater as every second slipped achingly away and begged for the only things that would satisfy our primitive libidos that insisted on descending the evolutionary ladder inebriated step by inebriated step.

Glasses filled, we sat in little man's lounge toasting the glory of baby oil and the female form. A battered, well worn video tape slowly penetrated the player in one glorious fluid movement and our senses were overwhelmed by a myriad of colours and sound. I felt my nausea rising as the performance began and I desperately tried to focus, tried to force it down and give the on-screen action my undivided attention. Was I sickened by what I was watching or the alcohol I'd consumed? My cerebral computer kicked in and silently bleeped and blopped its way through a list of simple calculations. I decided to blame it on the booze, as I'd never been very good at the whole drinking thing and it couldn't be the porno flick as I'd been a true believer in that particular sphere of entertainment since the age of fourteen and had the blisters and callouses to prove it. I decided that it was definitely the beer and vodka, that I shouldn't have mixed them in the industrial quantities that I had, but that's what men are supposed to do, so I shrugged it off. Admit nothing, deny everything, keep it down and hope you don't puke.

My fellow voyeurs had started to drool, and make inane comments as each frame flicked before them.

"She'd have it!!"

Quite possibly, but almost certainly not from you.

"Dirty fucking bitch, I bet she's filthy."

This much is evident from her so convincing role in this soap opera. Moron.

They didn't get it, they'd missed the point and the joke really was on them. It was a movie, a film, a slice of fantasy to ease the banality of day to day existence. It wasn't real no matter how much my companion's warped sense of actuality tried to convince them, and me, that it was. The whole scenario might actually have been funny if it wasn't so achingly pathetic.

Alcohol had transformed my drinking buddies into a pair of weekend weary love gods, and somewhere in their beer soaked psyches they become the gift that men wrongly think all women have been seeking since Eve reached for that first forbidden apple.

Pornography was just a job. It was just like every other nine to five – turn up in the morning, do what you've got to do, pick up your pay cheque and go home when the work's done. Artists use their hands and imagination, scientists, the intelligence they were born with and porn actors use their bodies. Everyone uses what they've got, the gifts they were given, to scrape by. You use what you've got and do what you've got to do in the hope that one day, you'll be allowed a taste of that elusive freedom that we all hear so much about.

"Morning Jane, how's it going?"

"Oh, the usual Dick, you know. Car needs a service, phone bill came through, and my mother's coming to stay next weekend."

Lights, camera, action. Cut, that's a wrap people.

"You wanna grab a coffee Dick."

"Yeah, that'd be great. Oh, wait, I've got to pick the kids up from school. Next time?"

"Sure."

Average people earning a living. But what a way to earn your money. You think so? If you fit tyres all week, it's the last thing on your mind at the end of the day. Imagine porn life take after take, day in, day out. Sex, or the thought of it, would make you sick. Violently ill.

"I've got to do this shit all day, and you want me to do it in my spare time as well? Fuck you!"

Where's the magic, the spontaneity, the lure of romance and spur of the moment? Killed by another service industry. You'd have to fuck an awful lot to get that pissed off with it right? How long did it take you to hate your job?

My marathon orgy of sex and alcohol over and my illusions shattered, I left, heard the birds singing and retched until my stomach felt like it was going to jump ship. I wiped my mouth, headed for home, wondering what Dick and Jane were up to and if they were happy or if they were just as miserable and broken as the endless succession of perverts, voyeurs and curious malcontents they entertained. I grinned and realised wherever they were, it had to be better than where I was, the humour never wearing thin, fooling generation after generation into confusing fantasy with reality. I vowed then and there that the poison known as alcohol would never contaminate my body again, and puked all over my shirt. Some things never change.

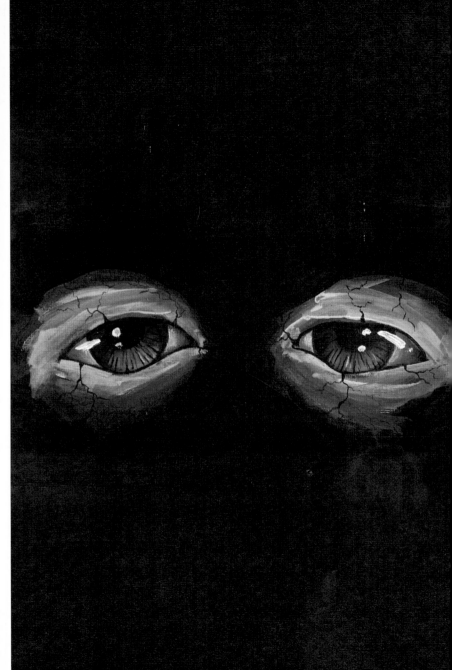

34

Time To Buy A Ray Gun

Bitterness, I could write a book on the subject, cross the T's and dot all the I's. A guaranteed motherfucking bestseller, the A-Z of misery and woe. Cynicism is a state of mind and nihilism the end product of a steady diet of irony and self-deceit. Most of us have spent a lifetime alone in an all you can eat diner, praying for an end. Along the way, the things that once inspired and filled us with a freshness and vitality that made it a crime to let a single day pass without rising to the challenge, were forgotten and cast aside, gathering dust in an abandoned corner of a cerebral closet. Buried under a mountain of gluttonous vanity. The struggle became mundane, an everyday thing that was done without knowing why. No identity and even less purpose made the accepted face of rebellion seem like an old friend, remaining only to remind us of how it once felt to be young. Young and full of hatred for the world in which we dwelt, for the injustices of humanity and crimes of the state. A never ending wheel on which we were condemned to spend eternity travelling its circumference. No forward movement, held in stasis above the jaws of defeat.

My reflection told me all that I needed to know.

The ravages of time had prematurely corrupted my face and started to turn what remained of my hair that simple shade of grey that stood as one with the boredom and the repetition of pointless existence. Dark circles lined my eyes, the product of too many sleepless nights offset by the nightmares of my own ineptitude. I no longer knew the person staring back at me from the bathroom mirror, pointing a withered finger at my barren soul, accusations of nameless deplorable acts filled my ears. The sweet music of maturity, repugnant yet strangely affectionate. Unable to meet its gaze, I sat down and started to peel away the layers that had built a wall of experience and denial, the stone foundations crumbling to dust as each one was carefully removed.

The values that had determined my every waking action now seemed trivial and worthless, fashioned from fear and naiveté rather than strength and contempt. Their puzzling influence was an anathema to my being, a contradiction of all I had been taught and all that I had learned. Jagged edges which would have to be smoothed down and filed away in order for them to have any meaning in a brave new world. They were disjointed and unfocused, an insane mesh of political rhetoric and social diatribe brought together from necessity, one feeding off the other as they both struggled to come to terms with their redundancy.

They lay on the floor, staring up at me, their pleas unnoticed as I continued my daunting task.

The addictions which had entered my life two by two, were next on the list. Their patriarch, head of the family winked at me as it crawled to the surface, dragging with it the memories of the subdued colours and peaceful death which were abundant with its usage. Heroin, the high priest of amnesia to whom I had dedicated a year of my life, was on trial once more as the jury delivered its unanimous verdict. Cast it down, throw it aside, no longer will it plague your dreams with images of self doubt. Let it hang by the neck until it is dead. The ease with which it was crushed under foot surprised me. We were no longer united by a bond of blood. The pupil had outgrown the master and found new pathways by which to escape his material chains. A high price had been paid but the debt was now paid in full, a blank page ready to be filled with substitute healing. Spreading them out, I retrieved only the vices which were required to aid my troubled conscience.

I recalled the songs of my youth and considered the role the movement known as punk now played in man's secular destiny. It had become that which it despised and had set out to destroy, forming too many subcultures to number in the process. Punk had drunk from the well of capitalism and the colour of money now flowed through the veins of the tamed beast. A pathetic circus act that would perform on command for the cruel and curious alike. It was no longer noble to suffer for your art in a vague battle against society, a notion that punk's disciples had once welcomed with open arms. A new breed of entrepreneurs had set the rules, outmoding those who had grown up with the scene. The whys and wherefores no longer mattered. That it was there was enough to drive it onward. A movement that had once prided itself on the communication of ideas and thrived on the fact that it was the sum of its parts, had allowed itself to be eviscerated and controlled by executives whose greed was only outweighed by their ignorance. I checked my baggage allowance and loaded the empty vessel, its relevance now a moot point.

Accessing my memory, the events that had shaped my destiny were a prerequisite if I was to reprogram the data base of my mortality. The stench of death and collection of individuals that had been attracted to me and vice versa, were the only luxuries that I would permit myself. Restored, renewed, invigorated and reborn I stared at the mirror and my reflection smiled back at me. The end will always justify the means because true beauty lies in the eye of the beholder.

212

35

The Great Equalizer

The Earth spins around the Sun, the tides rise, and the stars shine, circumstances change, and people move on. It's no use reflecting on the way things were or the way they may have been if the window of opportunity had only opened to invite you inside at the right moment, that's the sort of self-indulgent fantasy that never ends well. Occasionally though, it's nice to disappear into yourself and let memories wash over you and feel their familiar warmth, the one that starts in the pit of your stomach and slowly radiates out, touching every nerve and fibre and leaving no stone unturned.

The feel of an old letter, crumpled and creased, begs you to open it, survey the contents and think of all the yesterdays, the sweeping momentum that carries you to what you pray will be a better tomorrow. A couple of pills to ease the onset of rheumatic pains hastened by copious drug abuse, an over ambitious libido and scant regard for personal safety, a reading lamp, full moon and long summer evenings are all the elements needed to reconstruct a life that was long lost, one captured for posterity on yellowing paper folded into decaying envelopes.

They say that nothing changes between old friends except time. But I've never thought of time as being a constant. If it was, we wouldn't glimpse the past, while focusing on the moment at hand while gazing expectantly at the future and hoping that the lottery run by an obscure higher power finally calls your numbers. Predestination and the fallacies of heaven and hell would become nothing more than the disorganised thoughts of a final year theology student writing a dissertation, destined to be read by no one and cast aside in an instant of regret, nothing more than a failing grade that negates career options and the arduous rise to a position of influence greeted by dollar signs and a place in high society.

Old friends, the lives that touched yours and the lives that you changed, will never be forgotten as long as their influence remains, their faces thought of with compassion, their names spoken with a soft reverence that changes the tone of a conversation. If there was room for regret, or if I'd led a blameless life, I'd answer one charge and one alone. The failure to communicate which resulted in my losing touch with the people that meant more to me than life itself, bonds that were weakened by procrastination and an inability to commit to any task that took more than an hour to complete.

The days spent in the haze of a waking trance, trapped between the needle and a six pack, held together by your patience and forgiveness, Denise, I won't forget the debt that I owe and will someday repay. When others walked away, you stood firm and nothing would have shaken your resolve to help me through the pain and face the future with a sense of self-worth that replaced the loathing and fear that had previously filled my heart with dread. For a moment I thought you were lost to the world, the only connection to reality an intravenous drip and determination forged in steel. The envy I felt as you prepared to cross the threshold into blessed death was without measure, if you had needed a travelling companion I would have walked through fire to join you. What changed your mind I'll never know, but it made you stronger and the strength you gained was used to pull me back and show me how to fight, how to feel and how to love life, whatever the cost may be. Wherever you are and whatever you're doing, I hope you've found what you're looking for. Fuck knows you deserve to be happy.

Everybody has a twin, somewhere out there, thinking the same putrid thoughts and pushing the barriers to breaking point, and if fate decides that you should meet, the repercussions will be felt for generations to come. Afternoons spent in strip clubs, drinking for the sake of it and helping to keep the tobacco industry in the style to which it has become accustomed was a challenge handed down to only the bravest and most foolhardy. I know of only one other person with the stubborn arrogance and insolence necessary to rise to the task and embrace it with the flair and respect it deserves. Doug, I raise my glass to you, long may you shock the establishment and continue to be a thorn in the side of the politically correct. Brother there just wasn't enough time to do any more or compress the adventures of a lifetime into the time we had. You showed me the magnitude of the world, illustrating the similarities between far off places and how the same forces lie below the surface of every continent and how the dreams, desires and hopes of all men are linked, forming a chain that has stood the test of history, propelling us to a point that exists, unwritten, somewhere over the horizon. That, and how to bend the rules with a flourish that convinced all around you that you were on the side of the angels, too proud to care and too drunk to worry about petty ramifications. The trashed hotel rooms and women left in your wake would have made Genghis Khan look like a third rate snatch-and-grab man. Life was there to be lived, every second utilised and each minute used to the fullest. There isn't enough beer in the world or a country big enough to hold you or your attention for too long my friend. You're everywhere, a presence that can't be tamed or made to behave. Take it easy my man.

Letters are like a good book; you have to glance at them once in a while to remind yourself of where you've been and who you are. Take notes, because you can be tested at any time, and this is one course that offers you the chance to constantly absorb and adapt all you've learnt, applying it to the way you live your life. Experience all that you can, the final mark isn't a measure of how well you did, but rather an indication of how you treated others. Life 101 at the University of Planet Earth. Enrol if you've got what it takes, and if you haven't, take a nine to five and fade into the distance. It's that simple.

36

Roll Up, Roll Up...

You want to know what keeps me alive? What gives me a reason to carry on, to fight and to try to rise above the shit? Are you sure? It's you, every single last one of you. From the teenage hood hanging out on a street corner selling dime bags to underage single mothers to the presidents of the multinationals that consume developing nations and poison unborn children with the lethal effluents they create as they strive to shape a better tomorrow. Don't be embarrassed, stand up and show your face, credit where credit is due, all of you deserve to be recognised. After all, if it wasn't for your individual efforts, none of us would know what we were facing or who the real enemy was. So, ladies and gentlemen, one and all, I applaud your actions, knowing that as you diligently cope with adversity, your achievements continue to fuck everything up for countless generations to come.

Step back and look at what we've become. Not one of those cursory glances your boss expects you to give his yearly report, but a good, hard look at the point we've reached in our history. Can you see anything that's worthy of praise? Be honest, there's not an awful lot to feel good about is there?

If mankind was someone's idea of a continuous experiment, then they would have scrapped all their notes and research and started again. Failure in a closed environment isn't a problem, simply throw your results in the trash and resume your studies. Suck the whole bloody mess into a vacuum and jettison it into space.

Since we first assumed our place in the evolutionary chain we've made one mistake after another. How many wars have we fought in the name of peace? The list of our oxymoronic aggression and transgressions is growing all the time, add another page to the history of conflict as each decade speeds by. Why? Why, the human condition of course. Jealousy, one country wants what another has, buying into the fable of he who dies with the most toys and a never ending extended line of credit. Greed and the loss of profit is the only thing that motivates elected representatives for long enough to actually stand up and step into the breach to send young men and women off to die and kill other young men and women. Welcome to the twenty-first century, where greed is good and compassion is weakness. Last, but not least, we've got faith, the same faith that we blindly put in religion. My god is better than your god and if you don't believe me, I'll invade your home, burn it to the ground, murder your children and rape your women. I do this in the name of heavenly salvation. We're in the business of saving souls and following the word of the good book. It's all there in black and white hidden in the drawers of every hotel room, everywhere.

As we continued our journey to the top of the dung heap, we split into tribes and forged our identities, which over time gave rise to assorted cultures and ideas, each establishing man as a social animal. Distance meant that we didn't develop at a uniform rate, and as Europe became civilised, its natives set out to conquer the world and claim its territories for their own benefit. Civilisation is a strange beast with a specific set of ideals and if they aren't followed to the letter, then gentle persuasion and education are the tools by which it will craft the norm. Any and all indigenous peoples were dragged wholesale into the "civilised" idea of paradise which deliberately mistook a lack of social grace for stupidity, while trading land for trinkets as they dealt with the cavemen who held the keys to the kingdom of avarice. Cultural identity was decimated as Europe enforced its own set of values. Colonisation followed as the Western world grew. Who cares if they were here first, it's ours now and trespassers will be shot. Conform or die, a simple tutorial that was learnt the hard way by too many transgressors who sought nothing more than the freedoms they had lost. Nothing could stand in the way of progress as it rolled over the globe, gathering little moss as it continued on its thunderous path. Walk into the light and be reborn, there's only one way of life and that's the creed by which we live. When I think of all that we have lost due to ignorance and hostility, it always leaves the same question in its wake. Was it a price that we were ready to pay?

So, humanity reached the brow of the hill and dug in. Deep. It had taken us long enough to get there and sure as shit, no one was going to knock us off. Again, we threw our weight around and this time asserted our dominance over the animal kingdom. Can't take any chances so we'll keep them as pets and food and put them right in their place. Any deviation from our rule book, or if their appearance was a little out of the ordinary, we'd wipe them out. The town wasn't big enough for the both of us and we were the ones wearing the sheriff's badge. Our word was law and fuck anyone or anything that didn't agree with us. To be safe, we started destroying the habitats as well; cutting down the rainforests and polluting the oceans, making it hard to breathe so that they'd know who was pushing the buttons. The trouble was, as we deprived and depleted the animal republic we chipped away at the walls of our own arena, which removed our future possibilities two by two.

Answers? There are no answers, only problems

to overcome, solve and adapt to. I used to think that humanity was the answer, that we'd reach a point on the scale when we'd be able to do away with countries and nationalistic ideas and, united as one tribe, face all manner of adversity. Misplaced optimism and faith in my fellow men have always been two of my greatest faults, compounded by the fact that man stands on the brink of conquering space, ready to spread his sickness far beyond his earthly constraints. Sit enough monkeys at enough typewriters for long enough and eventually they'll produce the complete works of Shakespeare, which shows just how special we really are. We've barely begun and the Hare's going to run out of steam long before the Tortoise.

37

Long Cold Winter

Someone once told me that he knew how to commit the perfect murder. No physical evidence and no possibility of conviction. Like all second-hand information, I stored it and paid no more attention and filed it away with the rest of the junk mail, a growing cerebral mass desperately in need of a spring clean. Over the years I've assembled quite an extensive library of useless facts, conspiracy theories, personal secrets and dubious alibis. You name it, it's in there. Buried, hibernating and waiting for that single moment when its necessity would become inevitable. Contented and happy to let all things hold on to their investment in my mental time share, the concept of obsolescence has never been an issue. What's a use by date between friends? It's only some extra lettering, the small print on the packaging implemented by overly cautious legal departments.

Growing up, I'd read the stories of Robin Hood and the knights of old, and how their selfless deeds had made them the focus of legend as they followed the most well known of Vulcan credos about the needs of the many and those of the few. A simple, but seemingly perfect philosophy. Adapt your mistakes and use them to your advantage, make something of yourself and use your predilection for chemical dependency in the pursuit of redemption. Drugs and alcohol counselling was a job for the future, a service catering to the biggest growth industry on the face of the planet. Stress relief for the executives and middle management of the narcotic corporations that held the coming decades of human evolution firmly in their ever increasing grip.

Establishing base camp was easier than I'd ever imagined and with a minimum of training I was in the middle of a modern war zone, glorified by the media, in which the opposing factions faced each other across a desolate pill and syringe strewn no-man's land. I was an urban guerrilla walking the tight rope between good and evil, reassuring both, drawing up the conditions of a ceasefire that would never come into being. There was an element of danger that made the role more desirable, the adrenaline rush of knowing that no two days would be the same and your personal safety was in doubt at the best of times served as an opiate, the more you ingested, the greater the warmth and sense of well being.

I watched medical school graduates complain about their punishing sixty hour schedules and laughed, knowing that I was handling eighty and walking away untarnished. Or so I thought. Hell, this wasn't just a job it was a fucking adventure, a stroll on the wild side, a quick peek into the darkest realms of the seedier side of town. Nothing could touch or harm me, I was too far gone. An immortal among my contemporaries, bloated by the praise which they lavished upon my completed caseloads, I stood above the pack, the epitome of my vocation. To reach the pinnacle of this creed, I had spread myself thinly, the strings of the web drawn taunt. But the tighter they were pulled, the more liable they were to snap, all it needed was a little pressure in the right place and my fragile empire would collapse.

Without realising it, I had lost large segments of my personality, handing them out with reckless abandon to anyone who reached out to me. There was nothing left, I met each sunrise running on pure adrenaline, a desolate field that couldn't sustain its own existence let alone the lives that had come to depend on it. My downfall was a certainty, measured by the sands of time as they slowly trickled through my fingers. I was playing the waiting game with a loaded gun, and while at one in six the odds were in my favour, it was only a matter of time until I exploded in a megaton carry wave that would engulf all who surrounded me.

When it came, there was no refuge and no rest for the wicked. I've often heard about people who discuss serial killers, and the neighbours who one day just snapped, and they always say the same thing.

"He was such a quiet guy, it's the last thing in the world that any of us expected. But now that I think about it, there was always something about him that didn't seem quite right. Damn weirdos."

I was sat across from one of the leaches that had bled me dry, probing him about the theft of personal property that had gone missing two days previously. He looked up at me, pleading, a last ditch attempt to try and convince me of his innocence. I'd seen him with the items, knew he was guilty, so why the fuck was he lying to me? The mysteries of life have always escaped my insular world view. All the avenues had been travelled, all the corners explored, it was time to come clean and tell him what I knew.

"I know you took the stuff, just tell me why and I'll try and sort it out."

I was the voice of reason. Who could argue with that?

"Fuck off, you can't prove anything. Why are you accusing me when you're supposed to be helping me?"

Calling all gods and their minions, please give me the strength to rise above and not smite him down with great fury. Please.

"Come on, all I want to know is why you took it…"

His expression changed, a sly smile stretched out over his previously angelic face, a mask he'd perfected in penal institutions while being gang raped by overweight, middle aged guards who were trapped in an endless cycle of dark web fantasies.

"Yeah, I took the worthless crap. I don't know why. You're no better than the fucking pigs. At least they're honest about what they're doing."

When I woke up, I was holding him by his throat against the wall, a fist drawn back ready to strike. His screams could be heard throughout the building, a wailing banshee transfixing its listeners. I was pulled from him, the umbilical cord cut, and a desperate attempt made to calm both of us down.

He left the building promising a different punishment for each day of the week, all part of an insane vendetta, service charge included. Buy now, while stocks last. Eventually, faced with my actions, I had no choice but to go on indefinite leave. They called it nervous exhaustion, I called it release. Release from other people's shit, a chance to turn my gaze inwards, sort out my own rathole before clearing any other minefields. I'd like to think that it wouldn't have gone any further, but I know damn well that if I'd been able to recall what that guy had told me, then, as sure as the sky is blue, I'd have been cutting and slashing at the next unfortunate who crossed my path. All I could think of were the knots I'd been taught as a cub scout and the best way to replace a flat tyre. Animals hibernate for a reason and some truths are best left well alone.

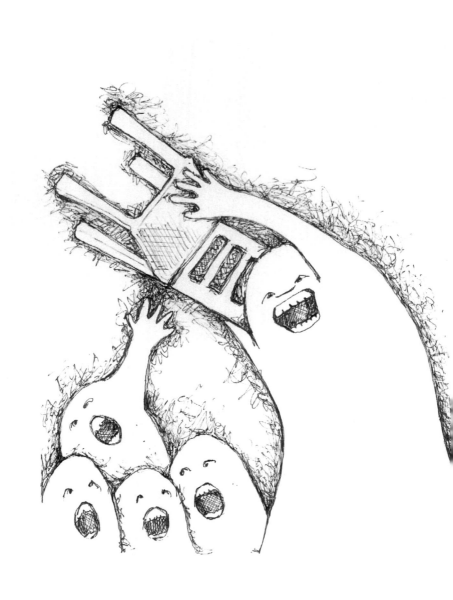

38

Sensitivity Training

Much as I might try to deny it in civilised circles, there's an unavoidable truth under whose burden I've been crushed since I was child. I am, for want of a better expression, an emotional cripple. My inability to express myself in anything other than my default settings of rage and functionality has subjugated, restricted and limited my interactions and the way I deal with people. Social situations are, for me, at best awkward and at worst a potential shit storm in the making. Mingling with those I don't know always ends badly, as strangers regard me as arrogant, obnoxious and rude, whereas in reality, all of those facets of my personality are exaggerated and projected as part of a front that I use in order to deflect the unwanted attentions of every single person I feel unfortunate enough to meet. Like the best of the best in the professional wrestling business who intensify their normal personalities tenfold in order to get over with the collective force of fandom, the misanthrope that I've played for so long has ended up becoming who I am; and now it's almost impossible for me to escape his influence and control. Don't misunderstand me, my lack of affinity is not due to some overwhelming hatred toward the rest of my species, it's more a case of not being able to relate to the vast majority of them on any level.

I wasn't always this way. I've been told that when I was little, I was incredibly gregarious, found it easy to mix and mingle and was content to spend time with, and enjoy the company of, my peers. I can't recall that being the case, but I'll take my family's word for it. They seem to think it used to be all sunshine, moonbeams, lemonade and lashings of ice cream. Maybe it was, but all that shit changed the minute my family uprooted me and moved to South Wales. I wasn't just the new kid, I was also small, skinny and ginger. And I talked "funny". My old man (convinced that the world outside of Liverpool regarded all Scousers as being subhuman) had also forbidden me from fighting as he thought it would only increase the inherent negative perception, and that if I ever fought anyone and he found out, he'd beat the holy hell out of me and give me such a hiding that it'd even make baby Jesus cry. You know when weather folks talk about a perfect storm, one created by an unlikely combination of factors, that wreaks havoc and destruction everywhere it lays its hat? That combination, all those implausible things happening at once in order to make something unique, that was me. I might as well have had "victim" etched into my forehead with a razor blade, and like a pack of starving wolves that have caught the scent of blood, it wasn't long before the animals descended like a horde on the weird little kid who couldn't fight back. And for next five years, my life became an endless cycle of daily mockery, beatings, humiliation, pain and psychological destruction. Some days were better than others. Some days there weren't any new bruises. Some days I didn't get my head slammed in a desk, repeatedly punched in the face or kicked in the balls for whatever reason my persecutors deemed fit, but even on the days when there was no physical pain, the mental torture, the perpetual insults – they continued unabated. That was my life and every damn day was the same.

But what about your friends I hear you cry? What about them? The few that I did have, they didn't want to get involved for fear that they'd end up sharing the same fate as me. Hell, sometimes, some of them even joined in and then the next day, pretended as though nothing had happened. But I remembered, because when you're caught in the eye of the hurricane, there's very little you can do except recall each and every indignity and disgrace, every moment of fear and shame when you've submitted to the inevitability of the devastation your life had become. As for my folks, well, they had enough of their own crap to deal with and were busy enough paying the bills and keeping the ship afloat, so didn't need to be burdened by my woes and misfortune. This left the teachers, who either didn't give a flying fuck about what happened to the "horrible brats" in their care or were too wrapped up in their own shit to even notice what was going on around them. Being a fast learner, I soon realised that I was the only person I could rely on and trust.

So, I hid away. I retreated into a world of books, film, television, role playing games and music, all of which provided solace and comfort to my increasingly battered and defeated soul. And it was there, in the comfort blanket they provided that I promised myself that no matter how much pain I endured, no matter how many times I was degraded, debased and dishonoured, I would not bend, break or become something that I wasn't in an attempt to lessen the onslaught or appease my tormentors. Sometimes I'd cry, sometimes I wouldn't, but I never, ever spoke. I just took everything they had to give, got up, brushed myself off and prepared for the next round.

Then one day, without warning, when I was twelve, something just snapped. A new face had rolled up and started to throw his weight around with me, started getting ready to throw what he thought would be a slurry of unanswered punches and before I knew what was going on, or what was happening, I hit him with a chair. Not one of those lightweight plastic, easily stackable disposable items that were designed for discomfort, no I hit with an ancient, made from the odds and ends that were left over from the Ark, built to last wooden throne. Then I hit him with it again. And again, and again, and again. Instead of the euphoria and release I expected to feel, I felt nothing. Nothing at all and where the fear, frustration and panic that permanently tied my insides in a knot used to dwell, there was an empty void. There was nothing. The next thing I knew, I was standing in front of the headmaster and my whole sorry tale of agony, grief and anguish was pouring out and he just sat there, listening intently, his attention focused entirely on my life story. Instead of the expulsion that the near hospitalisation of another pupil would normally warrant, I was given a two day suspension. I don't know why and I don't know how much he told, or what he said to, my parents, but instead of the existence ending pummelling that my father had promised to mete out to me should I ever raise a fist, let alone a chair, in anger, he just looked at me and without saying a word, gave me a sorrowful smile and nodded. He didn't need to say anything and neither did I. We both knew that my days of holding back, turning the other cheek and being a victim were over, that they had ended in the silent acceptance of everything that had happened.

Wish I could I say that there was a happy ending to the story, I really do, but five years is a long time and during that half decade, I learned everything that I ever needed to know about people. It taught me that I never wanted to feel that kind of hurt, that kind of abasement and ignominy ever again. It taught me that I would never let myself be humbled or made to feel ashamed of who I was, and am, ever again. It taught me to get a good offence in first, to come out swinging and if you ever do have to fight, it taught me that I needed to fight to maim, mutilate and kill and that the only way anyone would put me down was if they killed me, because I'd learned to always get up, no matter how much it hurt or how loud my brain was screaming at me to just stay down. I learned to live by three golden rules and I still adhere to them. Never bend, never break and never give in. I'd set the parameters of, and was comfortable in, my world. I still am.

There are hundreds of thousands of others who have endured the same things I had to, who were made to feel as worthless, weak and pathetic as I was made to and who continue, like me, to live with the legacy of what was done to them. Not everyone made, or makes, it through; and every single time without fail, I hear that someone else has been broken by abuse, my heart aches and I shed a tear. Because I lost count of the number of times that I came close to doing exactly the same thing.

I don't know who I was supposed to be before I became a victim of bullying and I never will. That person is long gone. He died in a five year flurry of meaningless, undeserved, punches, kicks and excruciating psychological anguish. All I know is who I am now. A barely functional, emotionally crippled survivor. And you know what? That's enough for me. It has to be.

39

It's Only Rock 'n' Roll...

I remember the moment that I knew it was over. It didn't hit me like a lightning bolt and it certainly wasn't the result of some life changing epiphany in which I was visited by Elvis returning from his intergalactic peace mission. It just happened. A tired, worn out, wheezing thought that rolled through my head, slouched down in the middle of my cerebellum, took a swig of whatever awful rotgut had kept it going for so long, belched and wheezed "I don't want to do this anymore". And looking around at the rest of the band, seeing the same bored expression in all of their eyes, I knew we were done.

For five years we'd given it our all, poured every single thing we'd had into trying to make our semi-rotted, stitched together carcass of minimal musical talent succeed and we'd failed spectacularly. In true Spinal Tap tradition we'd been through countless drummers, but where theirs had succumbed to spontaneous combustion and freak gardening accidents, ours had fallen by the wayside due to time honoured musical differences, traumatic brain injury and opiate addiction. We'd weathered the rhythmic onslaught and fought on, playing show after show to five people and the other bands on the bill while deluding ourselves into believing that spending time in a freezing cold rehearsal room, rehashing the same old songs over and over again in order to open someone else's gig was somehow "fun". It had become a habit. A dirty, terrible infatuation that was slowly consuming us, and after half a decade of pandering to its every whim, it was time to pull the plug.

Don't get me wrong, it hadn't always been that way. In the beginning, it had been an exhilarating, intoxicating ride. Creating "music" that screamed, howled and rallied against all that we collectively despised was the antithesis of the working week and granted the collective freedom that we misguidedly believed society had sought to deny us. Filled with venom and vitriol, our music was loud, fast and straightforward, we were a punk rock band with delusions of metal glory and a for an all too brief moment, it was magnificent. We submerged and submersed ourselves in barked vocals, blistering riffs, pounding snare beats, sweat, rage, beer and a seemingly endless cloud of illicit smoke. Buried in its embrace, the world outside of our practice space became the enemy, we started to believe the lies that we told ourselves and succumbed to the age old myth that it was "us against them". It infected and affected everything that we did and tried to do, as we convinced ourselves that the reason we weren't getting shows and a chance of recorded "fame" was because we weren't part of the "trendy" cliques that ruled over the punk rock scene with a rod of iron. Our outsider mentality became our safety blanket, drew us closer together, made us bitter, jealous and judgemental, and with no one else to direct our spite at, we eventually began, in the best passive-aggressive manner of twenty-something punk rockers, to channel it toward each other and in doing so, began the countdown to our own extinction.

And yet, in the middle of this nihilistic sea of self-loathing, we somehow became a pretty good live band. Up there in the heat of battle, the tunes weren't as important as the speed and energy with which they were delivered, and in a blinding orgy of nudity and self-harm that resulted in concussions, dislocated shoulders and more bruises, ligament and muscle damage than I care to remember, I lost myself. The music became less important than the physicality of performance, it became secondary to the inevitable intoxicating waves of pain and humiliation that boosted my adrenaline and fed my need to flagellate and punish myself, which as enjoyable as it was at first, became like everything else, a routine designed to shock that ultimately ate away at what little remained of my soul. I began to hate myself, to hate the band and worst of all, to hate those who'd embarked on the journey with me. It had to end. And on that last night, as I threw myself at some unsuspecting schmuck in the crowd, I looked around at my comrades in arms and knew that they felt exactly the same as I did. When the last song faded out and the lights went up, we didn't have to talk about it, we didn't have to sit down and discuss it. We all knew it was over. The dreams and ideas that had promised so much and delivered so little and had ended up becoming a waking nightmare were over. I was spent. They were spent. We were spent. It was over.

It was over. I made a vow, there and then, that I'd never do it again. And I never have.

40

A Paladin, An Elf And A Ranger Walk Into A Tavern...

"The room is pitch black. You can't see anything, but you can hear a clicking and shuffling..."

"I've got a torch. I'm going to light it. What can I see?"

"And while he's doing that, I'm getting ready to cast magic missile at whatever it is that's making that noise."

"The room seems to explode in light as your torch comes to life, and after quickly adjusting to the sudden illumination, you see a skeleton, dressed in rusting chain mail, sword in one hand, shield in the other. He charges toward you..."

And that's how my first game of Dungeons & Dragons started way back in 1983. Okay, so it didn't actually start like that; the obligatory meeting in a tavern, being hired by a rich merchant to find a fabulous jewel that he needed in order to pay for his daughters dowry (or so he told us gullible adventurers) and the descent into the dark depths of the dungeon in which said item was located all preceded that encounter. But it was my first taste of action in a game. The jolt of excitement that coursed through me, sending nervous shivers down my spine as I made my first combat roll was incredible; it was almost as though my ten year old self had suddenly stumbled across the purpose and meaning of life in that one random die roll that determined my fate on that cold, crisp Sunday afternoon. In that moment of imaginary planetary alignment and stellar conjunction, it all made sense to me and I knew that nothing would ever be the same again. I'd had my first taste of gaming and thus began my life long, sometimes secret, sometimes not, obsession.

It's hard to explain the appeal of, and what's so intriguing and exciting about, D&D and RPGs unless the person you're explaining it to knows what you're talking about or has actually played. In which case, you're already preaching to the armoured, hack 'n' slash choir as they know exactly what you're talking about. Trying to explain it someone who knows nothing about it though, that's something else entirely, as it does-n't matter what you say, it always sounds... well, sort of geeky. Which is fine and dandy, if like me, you're already a geek and proud to be so. Not so much for most people though, as every single time I've attempted to explain the all-encompassing magnificence of the game to them, have usually replied in one of three ways – sighed, given me that "there, there" look, rolled their eyes and muttered something along the lines of "Nerd", or, more commonly, they burst into uncontrollable fits of giggles, and when they've managed to catch their breath, have stared at me and just said "Really?" That answer, look and laugh when combined, for some reason unknown to the human psyche, makes any comeback, or thought of countering with a pithy anecdote almost impossible. And lastly, there's the response that I haven't encountered for nearly thirty years, which mainly involved getting punched in the side of the head and being told to "Fuck off". That was my favourite. Oh yes, I used to love that one best of all.

After constantly repeating the same futile exercise, you'd think I'd just give in, wave the white flag and admit defeat. If Einstein immediately recognised the insanity of repetition and expecting a different outcome, you'd think that after three decades that maybe, just maybe, I'd get it too. And if it was anything other than D&D, I probably would. However, the older that you get, the more you realise that there are very few constants in life, and that, more often than not, even friends don't number among them. Dungeons & Dragons, punk rock and comics though, they've always been there for me, and I for them. Relationships, trends, jobs and all that of boring nine to five rigmarole, it comes and goes, but D&D is as constant as the North Wind and the anger of Crom.

See, I could witter on about the connections to mythology, history and legend, the links to litera- ture and film, the creativity of imagination and how problem solving aids lateral thinking. I could talk about its escapist value and the need to find a way to relieve the increasingly confining and debilitating repression forced on all of us by a sys- tem we're imprisoned by and perpetuate through the enslavement of work. I could do that, but I won't. Because, it's all of those things and so much more, but at the end of the day, when you really get down to the nitty gritty and disassemble Dungeons & Dragons, it's a social thing. Like poker night. Except you don't lose any money, which means that you don't upset your partner, which means (theoretically) that you still get laid. And you get to slay monsters, explore far off dis- tant lands, encounter all manner of strange and marvellous creatures and places and bizarre people. You get to kill, maim and destroy without fear of recrimination or revenge and without worrying about doing serious gaol time for any misdemeanours or social faux paus you may or may not commit within the game. It's like playing a video game, but you get to hang out with your friends and avoid becoming a pasty loner afraid of the sun and everything beyond the confines of your bedroom door. You'll still be pasty and you'll still be terrified of the daunting power of Sol and all of the nasty, hidden dangers of the outside world, but at least you'll have friends. Dungeons & Dragons. It gets you laid, helps you make friends and it's cheaper and far less tiresome and boring than therapy. Go on, admit it. You want to play, don't you? Then pull up a chair, grab a D20 and let's begin.

Oh, and that skeleton? I smashed its skull in twain and made a necklace out of its teeth. That's how I roll...

41

Where Were You Scooby Doo?

The stink of cheap aftershave and broken, decades old ashtrays is what I remember the most. All I wanted to do was to go home, but that smell and the muted, whispered, empty threats that accompanied it made me their prisoner. I closed my eyes and tried to imagine being anywhere but there and as his hands clumsily fumbled their way inside my shorts, I thought about the welcoming aromas of Monday teatime and the Scooby Doo soundtrack that wrapped itself around them and desperately hoped that Freddy, Velma, Daphne, Shaggy and their faithful hound would magically appear to save me and take me away. That they'd take me anywhere as long as it was somewhere far away from there. As I felt his cold, uninvited touch and hot, fetid breath, I kept asking myself the same question over and over again: "Scooby Doo, where are you?"

I can remember the way the bark of the tree that he'd pushed me against felt on my lower back, its coarse, and uneven surface digging its claws into my skin as he frantically pulled my shorts down. I can remember the way the moss and leaves felt under my feet, like a vast sponge spread across the forest floor as my underwear emblazoned with the symbol that meant hope on a faraway world brushed past my ankles. I remember the solitary tear that traced a forlorn path down my face as he pushed a finger inside me, the shock of it happening outweighing the pain of his ragged finger nail scraping and ripping me as he rammed his digit as deeply as he could before his cracked knuckles hammered against my naked buttocks. I remember thinking that my time was quickly ticking away, that my final moments would be filled with fear and agony and that I'd be left broken on the of side of an unremarkable hill on a woebegotten farm somewhere in the middle of nowhere. That I'd be forgotten and left to fade into the scenery, that it was my own fault because that's what happens when you're soft, when you don't want to be where you are and when, scared of what might happen if anyone saw you crying, you run away to hide only to be found before you were ready and discover that some monsters are all too real and that the masks that they choose to wear let them pass untroubled in the world.

I tried to drift away, to be anywhere but where I was, certain that my end was coming when he grabbed my hair, pulling and yanking it hard enough to make me whimper as he slowly and purposefully pushed my head toward his groin. He kept whispering something over and over again, but caught somewhere between fearfully preparing for my impending doom, the sound of my heart pounding so fast that I thought it was going to burst out of my chest and flashes of the Mystery Machine rushing to my imaginary rescue, I can't recall what it was that he was saying. Nor do I ever want to.

My eyes were closed tight in a vain and fruitless attempt to stop the tears flowing, because somewhere in the back of my mind, I was convinced that if I couldn't see what was happening, then maybe it wasn't real, that none of this was and that I'd wake up at home, having fallen victim to a substantive, fourth wall shattering nightmare. I kept telling myself that right up until the moment he tried to thrust himself into my mouth. Maybe if I'd acquiesced the first time he tried, he wouldn't have slapped me, my ears wouldn't have started ringing and my knees wouldn't have buckled and left the entire weight of my body suspended by my hair which he still gripped in his other hand. Maybe. Maybe not. Maybe the taboo thrill of resistance was just the second act in his sordid little game. Maybe he just liked hurting me and maybe he revelled a little longer in my pain and the quivering tingle of additional excitement that it gave him. Maybe. I've always been a quick learner, and the second time he tried, terrified of being struck again, I gave in.

As he heaved himself back and forth, groaning

with every swing of his hips, I started to gag. I felt my stomach begin to convulse and prayed to whatever deity had placed me in harm's way that day to not let me throw up, to not let me upset him or make it worse, to just let him finish whatever it was he was doing and that when he killed me, I hoped it wouldn't be as painful as it was when the supporting players were ungraciously removed from the story to provide additional emotional depth and motivation for the hero in the trashy afternoon films that I'd wasted my young life watching. I wasn't even the hero in my own story, I was a third rate sidekick who wasn't worth keeping around for the sequel. As his passion gained momentum and surged toward climax, I imagined that my tormentor must have realised this and drew an ever increasing modicum of satisfaction from it.

That taste. That salt laden, sour milkshake taste that's like swallowing seaweed while submerged in the ocean and drinking in the heavy atmosphere halfway through a busy summer's day in Blackpool, never goes away. It lingers in the back of your mind, emerging only in those moments when you're cold and shivering in the dark as the spectres of your past chatter quietly in the background. Rising unbidden when panic sets in and the inexplicable urge to vomit takes over, that taste stays with you for a lifetime. The unwanted revulsion of a long forgotten evening that nudges at the edge of your memory, haunts your restless dreams and refuses to leave no matter how much you beg. The first drink that you dare not tell anyone about lest you drown in the sin of admission.

Satiated, he pushed me aside, glared at me in disgust and growled...

"If you ever tell anyone about this you little fucker, I will fucking kill you."

I believed him then and I still believe him now. Thankful to just be alive when every atom of my being had told me that I was going to die, I vowed then and there to never to mention it, that I would never tell anyone of the indignity and shame that a frightened, pubescent child was subjected to when all he wanted was someone to tell him that it would be okay, that the world wasn't as daunting as it appeared to be and that there was nothing to be afraid of. But that would have been a lie, because there was everything to be fearful of, and on a becalmed and still July night, reality showed me just how terrifying it could really be.

On that lonely hill in the middle of nowhere, curled up in the detritus of the forest, I died the little death of shame and secrecy. I began to sob, tried to forget what had happened and for three and half decades those unrequited, brief minutes of molestation have festered and gradually poisoned all that I was, am and ever will be.

And lying there, lost, confused and alone, the only thought that bounded into every corner and down every avenue of my mind was: "Where were you Scooby Doo? Where were you when I needed you...?"

42

A Long Time Ago...

"What's wrong?"

I couldn't tell her. I couldn't even look her in the eye. I was too busy trying to stop myself crying, too busy trying to stop the tears flowing and stop those little hitching, twitching, spasmodic breaths that reduce you to a blubbering mess from taking control of my every muscle.

"It's a father and son thing isn't it?"

I nodded dumbly, focusing on some indefinable point on the darkening, distant horizon while vainly and desperately choking back the flood that threatened to drown me in repressed sorrow and soak what was left of my soul in the memory of a thousand yesterdays.

"It's okay. Let it go, let it out."

So, I did.

Of course, it was a father and son thing. How could it not be? The whole damn saga is about the convoluted and, all too often, complicated father son relationships. I don't know how the Beard felt about his old man, but having seen *Star Wars*, *The Empire Strikes Back* and *Return of the Jedi* more times than I care to count, and should have done, I'm fairly sure that they didn't have a straightfor-ward, easy going, good natured, share a few a beers while having a laugh or two kind of bond. In fact, I'm fairly certain that they probably shared the same sort of affinity with each other as most of us do, and did, with our dads. That is, a messy, entangled, confusing mixture of pride, loathing and machismo that more often than not, takes us a lifetime to figure out and come to terms with.

I had, as I got older, what most folks would call a fractious and volatile kinship with my father. As punk rock, women and a ridiculous desire to rebel against anything and everything slowly consumed me, we began to butt heads more and more, eventually reaching a point where we nearly stopped talking completely. Maybe we would have if it hadn't been for Star Trek and all of the other wonderful things that he shared with me when the world was still a scary, brilliant, exciting place filled with mystery and endless possibility. The things that we could always fall back on, the things we could rely on to bring us back together no matter how bad things became. Chuck Yaeger. Doctor Who. Gagarin. Titov. Shepard. Grissom. Glenn. Gemini. Apollo. Verne. Heinlein. Perry Rhodan. The V8. Marvel. DC. Hammer Studios. EC Comics. Disney. And Star Wars. There was always Star Wars. That was our "thing". Always had been, always was and always will be.

Seeing Star Wars was the first time I remember making a connection with my father. Hell, I think it may well have been the first time that the two of us had been alone together and didn't have to rely on anyone else to make small talk or deal with any of the uncomfortable, difficult, daily stuff that leached the life out of every parent determined to do the "right thing" for their kids. On that night in early January 1978, none of that mattered. It was just us and a galaxy far, far away. From the screen being blocked out by a Star Destroyer entering high orbit above Tatooine to the destruction of the Death Star, it was perfect. Star Wars. My Dad. Me.

But the original trilogy also defined, and acted as a metaphor, for our relationship. As I grew up, there was the desire to escape the home that I'd grown up in, one governed by authority that I had to rebel, and fight, against in order to escape, the refusal to accept that I could be anything like him and the desperate battle to prove that I wasn't, before eventually coming to terms with all that had happened, both good and bad, and making peace with each other in his final moments. Star Wars. That was always our thing.

Thirty-eight years after I first entered a smoke filled auditorium with my dad and let my imagination travel through the murky blackness of space, I finally returned to that galaxy where it all began. The screen creep started, and I swear my old man was there with me, in spirit at least. Grinning from ear to ear, whooping with joy as the Falcon took to the skies again and laughing with abandon and absolute pleasure as the First Order, much like the Empire did in *Star Wars* when confronted by the Rebellion, fell to the forces of the Republic. And I turned to face him, and for a fleeting moment, he was there, sitting next to me. The tears began to flow, and I smiled. Star Wars was still ours. It always has been and always will be.

It's a father and son thing.

43

It's Pronounced "Hardcore"

"Like dominos stacked in a line..."

Fixation can be a terrible burden to carry, but it's one that I've been forced to embrace and learn to live with. Due to a slightly devastating combination of personality type and OCD, I've a tendency to focus entirely on the things that appeal to me and more often than not have ignored the things that have no immediate impact or influence on my existence. Which is why I can quote the genealogy of obscure eighties hardcore bands without hesitation, will happily waste hours of your time explaining historical cause and effect, am uncomfortably familiar with the chronology of TSR Games, talk about Moon Knight and Captain America like they're old friends, have an encyclopaedic knowledge of genre fiction and the mythology of certain science fiction franchises, but don't have the first clue how to wallpaper a room, can't hang a door, have no grasp of basic DIY and haven't mastered any of the life skills that would have enabled me to have a satisfying, if somewhat boring, real world career.

Oh sure, I could take the easy way out and blame

everything on a succession of head injuries and multiple concussions and wilfully bad life choices which were made because of a stubborn refusal to accept that anyone else might better understand any given situation. Yeah, I could definitely do that and to be honest, both have probably played some part in my need to fixate on things, but at the end of the day I also have to accept that it comes from me being me. It's just the way I've been built, the way my brain is wired and that hard as I might try to shake that particular imp off my back, it's always going to be there and going to be part of who I am. That's why I learned to draw it close to me, to attempt to utilise it in a positive way in order to enhance my minute to minute, hour to hour, day to day journey instead of letting it control my every waking moment and by doing so, make me eternally miserable. It took a while, but I've finally managed to take the reins and now I'm the one in the driving seat instead of being the stuttering, stumbling, screaming moron stuck in the back of a barely controlled yellow taxi piloted by my gibbering, hysterical cerebellum.

While learning how to become somewhat proficient at Human 101 hasn't been an easy ride, it hasn't all been bad. Heck, being a slave to fixation has had more than its fair share of entries in the win column over the years with one of the more notable triumphs being my tendency to hone in on record labels with laser sharp focus, and become more interested than was probably good for my health or sanity. If a label released a record by a band that I liked, it'd pop up on my radar. If they put out albums by a couple of bands that I liked then I'd start actively searching for their releases and if they released three artists or records that featured on my obsessional daily menu, then that was it, game over, I had to know anything and everything about them. Epitaph, Revelation, Combat Core, Fat Wreck Chords, Victory, Lookout, New Age Records, Manic Ears, Peaceville, Earache, Taang, Dr Strange, the names of labels on my list goes on and on and on, but now that I'm behind the wheel, I've been able to track the compulsive route back to the beginning and isolate the label that started this particular avenue of obsessive behaviour. Hawker Records.

In the grand scheme of things, Hawker's existence was brief. And by brief, I mean, blink and you'd miss it brief, and the size of its catalogue reflected its short lifespan. Beginning as the last days of 1987 were fading away, or at near enough the stroke of midnight on New Year's Day 1988, depending on which internet rumours you believe or take to heart, Hawker started, and ended, its life as a hardcore imprint, or sub-label, of Roadrunner Records and supposedly (again, this is entirely dependent on who and what truths you choose to put your faith in) got its name from Cees Wessel's, the man who founded and owned Road-runner, inability to pronounce "hardcore" properly. Picking up on this, some bright spark, an intern or some other lowly cat who was no doubt treated like crap and probably beaten with bootleg Venom albums if he or she didn't do their job properly, named the label accordingly. I like to think that they did it to spite the boss man, but he was probably in on the "joke" and approved wholeheartedly as he started to imagine all of the extra zeros that he hoped Hawker would add to his already staggeringly huge bank balance. Because those kind of money making insider giggles are the kind of humour that rich people love and wholeheartedly approve of.

Anyway, I'm drifting off point. Where was I? That's right, Hawker's fleeting hardcore life. The label started in '87/ '88 and closed its doors and hung up its Converse, which barely had time to see any pit action, at the end of 1989. And in the two years that it chased bands, pressed records and did what all the vinyl purveyors in the music business do, it managed to release six albums. That's right, six. Right about now, every other obsessive reading this is probably thinking: "That sounds about right, the cult aspect of its tenure and the fact that it only introduced a sextet of albums to the world lends credence to the reason for your passion", and I'd agree with, and back, that statement one hundred and ten percent if I liked all six of the records that it released. But I don't, so I can't get behind the valid reason my brothers and sisters in crazy have offered up to explain my Hawker devotion. I only like four of the records that Hawker saw fit to release. Okay, no that's wrong, I "love" four of the six Hawker records, and the fact that I still get sweaty palms, chills down my spine and the hairs on the back of my arms still stand up whenever I play one of them is almost certainly the reason that I originally went, and am still, ga-ga bat shit mental over, and about, Hawker Records.

Next, the debut long player by the Pagan Babies from Philadelphia was the first time I bumped heads with a band on Hawker. I hadn't even heard of them before I picked it up and the only reason I did was because of a review I read somewhere by a writer whose word, according to my indomitable teenage logic, was law. I figured if he said it was good, then it must be good and so I grabbed it, took it home and started playing it. In fact, I played the shit out of it. That record didn't leave my turntable for a fortnight. Bridging the gap between the burgeoning NYHC scene and the more traditional early eighties West Coast Hardcore sound, *Next* spoke to me like few records had before and apart from the bass player who looked like he could have been a member of Crucifix, the Pagan Babies didn't look like "punks". They looked just like every kid who was drawn to the hardcore scene by bands like Bad Brains, Youth of Today and Gorilla Biscuits did. They looked like I did. And while it seems crazy now, back then that made their music even more important to me. After all, if they could do it, it meant that I could, which was the embodiment of the hardcore ethos. It was an ideal that was perfectly encapsulated by The Spermbirds in *Get on the Stage* and one that was staring directly at teenage me from the inner sleeve of *Next*.

The funny thing is though, try as hard as I might, I don't remember who the critic whose words meant so much to me back then was, or which publication it was that I read the review in. This forgotten muse had led me to a band who reinforced my belief in hardcore and I can't even recall his name, a fact that was probably pushed out of my head to make room for some trivial piece of useless third hand information that only reached me after it had passed ghost like through a horde of higher up the food chain scene folks. And as well as being the band which introduced me to Hawker, the Pagan Babies was also the first band that made me aware that the label was "cursed". Oh, you don't believe in "curses"? That's cute. Stick around kids, and maybe, just maybe like Luke did after a couple of ball breaking training sessions in the swamp with Yoda, you will. For now though, I'll stay on target and move on to the second chapter of my Hawker story and come back to the dark hardcore voodoo that the label wove into its bands' DNA later.

After a brief sojourn in Philadelphia with the Pagan Babies, Hawker looked East, targeted the home of hardcore, New York City and set its sights on Token Entry. While they may not be the sort of slam happy household name that Agnostic Front, Cro Mags, Madball and Sheer Terror have become, Token Entry's members did stints with the Gorilla Biscuits, went on to form Black Train Jack and Redemption 87 and even started Chunksaah Records, a label which became the home of, among others, The Bouncing Souls. Token Entry signed on the dotted line with Hawker for their second album, *Jaybird*, which is, in my humble opinion, their defining moment. While it's often, quite rightly, seen as being a record of two halves with the first half (or A and B sides as they used to be called) being considerably better than the second, the songs that comprise the opening chapter of the album are still, thirty years after they were first released, five of the most incredible "hardcore that makes you want to hit the dancefloor" songs ever recorded.

Kicking off with *The Fire*, Jaybird slaps you

around like a coked up bouncer with its combination of sing-a-long choruses, infectious breakdowns and high velocity tunes that don't ease off the gas until the closing moments of *The Whip*. They turned my teenage brain inside out and made me swear that one day, I'd get to dive off the stage that Timmy Chunks, Ernie Parada and company were smashing to bits with their home grown, Astoria brand of NYHC. Three decades later, I'm still waiting to fulfil that promise, as while they lasted a little longer than the rest of their Hawker brethren and released a final album, *The Weight of the World*, at the beginning of the nineties, they called it a day soon after. Were they also victims of the "infamous", and made up by me, Hawker curse? I couldn't possibly comment ladies and gentlemen and will leave that sort of idle speculation entirely up to you.

After that, it was time for Hawker to bounce, to quote Roger Miret, "from the East Coast to the West Coast". No For An Answer, the next band to join Roadrunner's Hardcore offshoot were a straight edge band from Orange County whose frontman was the one and only Dan O'Mahony. While they were by no means the first band from their scene to proclaim adherence to the edge, they were the first band that I heard from OC and they had a profound effect on the much younger, and much more arrogant and obnoxious, version of me. They didn't make me want to turn my life around and abandon cigarettes or alcohol as I was a firm believer in the Bill Hicks and Lee Ving philosophies concerning both, nor did they change my view of casual encounters with the female of the species, as even though they weren't exactly frequent, those dalliances were the highlight of my teenage years. What can I say; I lived in a town that had a Catholic Girls' school. And yes, all those things that you've heard, all the whispered tales of what happens behind convent school walls, they're all true. Because girls just want to have fun.

No. What No For An Answer taught me was this. When Dan growls, you listen. You listen because you'd better believe that he has something important to say as he's not the kind of person who wastes his words or embellishes falsehoods; and he's definitely not the kind of chap who suffers fools gladly, sadly or in any other way you, I or any else, can think of. *A Thought Crusade* was a rough and tumble collision of the music that had influenced its creation. Uniform Choice, the original wave of DC bands, the emerging New York and Connecticut straight edge sound, they were all present in its grooves, all of which were driven forward by Dan's unmistakable howl and that record, it began my lifelong devotion to both the OC sound and the bands that their charismatic, fiercely intelligent and direct vocalist would go on to sing for. And Dan hasn't let me down yet. Carry Nation, Speak 714, John Henry Holiday, 411, Done Dying, the bands he's played with have consistently blown me away and it all started with No For An Answer. It all started with Hawker Records.

Then came the fourth and, for me at least, last of the seminal Hawker releases. Having forced me to swear allegiance at the altar of O'Mahony, the not so little label that could (oh come on, they were bankrolled by Roadrunner and their eighties metal explosion cash so they weren't as small as they pretended to be) then dipped their toes in the raging maelstrom of crossover and plucked a scrappy, energetic crew of misfits and malcontents out of the Boston scene and threw them into a studio. And the Wrecking Crew, for that was what the delinquents from Massachusetts called themselves, handed Hawker *Balance of Terror* in return. It was a swift uppercut that arrived during the last days of the first wave of Crossover and helped to stoke the last heat from the dying embers of its fire, allowing it burn brightly for just a little longer. Part Agnostic Front, part Jerry's Kids and with a whole load of thrash attitude, they appeared on the horizon, challenged any and all comers and for a kid who lived on the other side of the big pond, a thousand leagues away from America, they seemed to vanish in less time than it took for me to spin *Balance*. Yet thirty years after the fact, I can remember first hearing them and feeling that rush of excitement in every nerve ending of my being as they tore out of the crappy speakers of my cheap stereo and how disappointed I was when I eventually discovered that they'd called a halt to their wrecking and disbanded their crew. One record did all that. Hawker did that.

I know that chronologically I've almost certainly got the release schedule wrong. I know that and I don't care. This was the order that I discovered Hawker Records and its bands and records in and it's the order that's indelibly stamped in my mind. It's my order. It's not necessarily the right one, nor is it in all likelihood, one that anyone else will agree with. None of that stuff matters. What matters is that a slightly obscure label born on an idle whim changed my life forever, sparked something in me in that I didn't know existed but has driven me in a positive, and at times overwhelmingly negative, fashion ever since. What matters is that it released four records that I'm still bewitched by, and listen to, far more that I really should, three decades after they initially emerged. That, boys and girls, is how legends are forged, myths are born and the key to how immortality is created. Because that music, now that it's out there and as long as one person is as rabidly zealous and fervid about it as I am – it'll live forever.

Normally, it'd be at this point where things would be neatly tied up with some sort of pithy closing statement or sentence that regurgitated a tired old eighties cliché about how hardcore is a celebration of unity, come one, come all and all that other tired old jibber jabber that anyone who's been around the scene for a while knows is just hot air and rhetoric. The truth is hardcore is what you make it. The more you put into the scene, the more you'll get out of the scene and my fixation with Hawker has meant that all the energy I've invested in those four records has been repaid tenfold. Not just by the music, but by the things that music has enabled me to do and the people I've met because of it.

But the Hawker story doesn't end there. If you were paying attention earlier, you'll recall that I mentioned that there were six records released by the label and just because I don't dig them, it doesn't mean that you won't. Actually, that's not quite true. The fifth Hawker release, by Jones Very the band formed by Vic Bondi after Articles of Faith threw in the towel(s) for whatever reason they saw fit, *Words and Days* is actually pretty good. It just took me twenty-five years to "get it" and actually enjoy it for what it is; a great post hardcore, post punk, doing your own thing whatever that may be collection of songs. And just because it took me a quarter of a century to get there with Jones Very, it doesn't mean that it'll take you anywhere near that amount of time. So, go on, be adventurous, give them a spin, I dare you.

Then there was number six, *Free for All.* A compilation that featured all of the bands on the label but as I'm kind of locked into the weird, self-induced mind set that hardcore compilations begin and end with *Where the Wild Things Are* and *New York City Hardcore: The Way It Is*, just like every other hardcore and punk rock label compilation that's crossed my path in the last thirty something years, it's never floated my boat. Or even come close to doing so. Although, I have been sort of tempted by it a number of times, but only because it's the only Hawker release to feature Rest In Pieces, the only band on *Free for All* who didn't release an album on Hawker.

Yes, it is "the" Rest In Pieces. The one from New York that was born when Armand from Sick Of It All decided that he wasn't doing enough hardcore stuff. And, Craig Setari, just like he's done with every other big hitter from the Big Apple core scene, also, at one point, played bass for Rest in Pieces. Apparently, it's an unwritten rule of the NYHC scene. Either Craig or Walter has to pass through your ranks or no one will come to your shows. Don't blame me, I don't make the rules,

I'm just repeating what I was told. At a secret Hardcore Club meeting, held behind the Planet X on show night, presided over by an "official" nominated by Al Barille, appointed by Ray Cappo and sworn in by Ian Mackaye, an official who made everyone who was there that night swear an oath of secrecy that couldn't be broken until the Gorilla Biscuits returned. I know what you're thinking; you're thinking that I just made all that stuff about Hardcore Club up. Maybe I did and maybe I didn't. Maybe the first rule of Hardcore Club is the same as the first rule of Fight Club. Or maybe it isn't and maybe there's no such thing as Hardcore Club.

Oh, and finally, one thing I definitely didn't make up was the Hawker curse. I promised I'd tell you all about it and being a man of my word, I'm going to do exactly what I swore I would. So here it is – how many of the bands who put their faith in Hawker went on to achieve everything that they could, and should, have? That's right kids, none of them did. For reasons known only to them-selves, those bands disappeared, fading away like the last light of day, when Hawker folded. Imagine what might have happened if they'd released those records on other labels, how things might have been and how different the scene would be. Now that's something worth fixating on...

44

My Pal George

Every story has a beginning. Everybody's journey starts somewhere. Nobody emerges from the womb fully formed, knowing exactly who they are with a crystal clear vision of what they're destined to do and who they're supposed to be for the rest of the time they walk the Earth. Each and every one of us is just a blob of shapeless clay waiting for inspiration to lead us out of the darkness of mundanity and into the light of absolute, individual certainty. There's a moment in everyone's life when they encounter something or someone that changes their perspective, forever alters their outlook on life and makes them realise what it was, and is, that they're meant, and want, to do with the rest of their days. My epiphany began with George Tabb.

In the summer of 1992, I was teaching riflery at a camp in Pennsylvania, instructing small children in the use of firearms. Until then, all I'd ever wanted to be was a soldier and having just been informed by the army that I was medically unfit to serve due to a back injury that I'd suffered two years previously, I was, for all intents and purposes and as the Jerry's Kids' song so succinctly put it, lost. That news had hit me like a drunk swinging a sledgehammer in a china shop, smashing all of the plans that I'd made and goals that I'd set for myself. I was devastated, had no idea what I wanted from life anymore, no purpose or ambition and had taken the instructor's job to try and get some breathing room in an attempt to figure the life stuff out. Not that it wasn't fun, it was. It was a whole lot of fun, it was almost more fun than any person should ever be able to have without exploding and spraying their nearest and dearest in all manner of viscera and bodily bits and pieces. But all the fun I was having didn't change the fact that the days until my contract was due to end had begun to tick down and I was floundering toward the future like a rudderless hippie.

Which is when fortune, for once, smiled on the not so brave, arriving in the form of a care package that had winged its way across the Atlantic Ocean from "dear old" Blighty. Tucked away in the parcel were a couple of issues of Maximum Rock 'n' Roll, the long running punk magazine that was based in San Francisco. While I'd periodically dipped in and out of reading it for the band interviews, scene reports and record label news, I'd never bothered even looking at the columns before those issues turned up. It was probably the dearth of other available reading matter on the camp that finally forced me to peruse MRR in greater depth, and I recall being intrigued by a feature that was in one of the issues called something like "Punk's Thirty and Still Doesn't Give a Shit" in which a whole bunch of punk rockers and scenesters who had sailed past the big three-o were interviewed about their involvement in, and with, the punk rock scene. And the only interviewee I can still vividly recall from the feature was George Tabb. That was my first encounter with the man who gave me my sense of direction back.

Fast forward a couple of years and I was an avid MRR subscriber, but I was no longer interested in the bands that it talked to, the scenes that it reported on, the tittle tattle and "she said, he did" conjecture and rumour that filed its letter pages and the gossip about which labels were cool and which ones sucked because of some vaguely offensive political statement that the owner had made when drunk a decade previously. No, the reason I read Maximum Rock 'n' Roll was the columns. And one column in particular – George Tabb's Take My Life Please. It was both the first and last thing that I read every issue, as I figured go in on a high and end the same way. Take My Life was a series of autobiographical tales and stories from George's life, that always made me laugh and while it seemed like, on the surface at least, George was living the punk rock dream, when you dug a little deeper, there was so much more substance to, and behind, everything he wrote. His columns were funny, acerbic, self-deprecating accounts of band life, his family and wonderfully strange people he bumped into and situations that the shortest serving member of the Ramones found himself in. They were astonishing, stylistically unique, witty and engaging and made me realise that you didn't have to create detailed alien worlds to tell a story, you just had to write what you knew. Reading George's columns made me want to write because he made me realise that everybody has a story, you just had to find a way tell your own tale. So, I did.

Hit the fast forward button again, a few more years passed, and I had a box filled with the first badly edited edition of my debut novel. I think I had something like ten copies of it and in an all too rare moment of bravado, I decided that I'd send a copy to George, because he was, after all, the guy who'd inspired me to become a writer. I wrapped a copy up, popped it in the post and didn't think about it again until I read Take My Life Please two months later. And in the footnotes, George had written about my book. He'd not only read it, he'd liked it. Heck, he'd loved it and he said so. Right there in his column. It was one of the happiest moments of my life and then and there, working on the strike while the iron is hot principle, I decided to ask George if he'd be interested in being interviewed for Mass Movement. I sat down, did my best nonchalant e-mail thing and in less than thirty minutes, George replied and said "You betcha", or something along those lines. I'm old and it was a while back. Give me a break.

Then, just as I was getting ready to send the interview, 9/11 happened and everybody's world got turned upside down. But the ones that flipped the fastest and the hardest were the worlds, and lives, of the people who lived and worked in New York City. People like George Tabb who lived less than half a mile from the twin towers of the World Trade Centre. Having been that close to the epicentre of the attack changed everything for George, and trying to regain some semblance of normality, he moved away from the city and headed West. After he started feeling some of the physical effects caused by the collapse of the World Trade Towers, George became a leading, and one of the first, advocates of a movement that was based on discovering the truth about what was happening to the close quarters survivors of 9/11; why they were getting sick and what caused it.

Time passed and I got back in touch with George, we did the interview and I sent him a copy of the issue of Mass Movement (this was back in the days when it was still a print magazine) that he was featured in. He kind of liked it and told me

so, and so in another moment of rare opportun-
ism and ridiculous bluster, I asked him if he'd like
to write, and become a columnist, for Mass
Movement. An hour later, he was signed up and
ready to go. I think that was my favourite, along
with running George's debut column, moment in
Mass Movement's history and it was the start of
my friendship with the man who had inspired me
to write and become a journalist. Honestly, as
incredible as I thought he was before I knew him,
nothing prepared me for how kind, warm and
generous a person he really was, and is. George
was also the reason that we managed to snag an
interview with the Village People for Mass Movement. That's right kids, the Village People were in
Mass Movement and it was all thanks to George
Tabb. True story.

For nearly a decade, things ran pretty smoothly,
or at least as smoothly as they ever do in Mass
Movement land. George sent in his columns, I ran
them and read them and was always amazed by
how easy and natural his stories were. We talked
via e-mail and every time we did, I had to pinch
myself to make sure that I wasn't dreaming and
that this was really happening. That George Tabb
was my friend and that he was writing for my
magazine.

And then George got sick. Really, really sick. His
illness, which was and is directly attributable to

the events of 9/11, made him re-examine his own mortality and priorities; and not having the energy that he used to have, he stepped back from a lot of his writing commitments, Mass Movement included. I understood at the time and I understand now. I can't even begin to imagine coping with all of the fallout from that fateful day with the same stoicism and strength that George has, and I'm proud of him and feel honoured that I'm able to call him my friend. He was, and continues to be, an inspiration and is the best, most naturally gifted writer I've ever known. If you haven't read his books, you owe it to yourself to do so. They might just change your life. Oh, and one last thing. George, in case you've forgotten, or I've been negligent and not told you this enough during all of the years we've known each other, you rule.

288

45

The Mysterious Machinations Of The Phantom Flan Flinger

It's the Phantom Flan Flinger's fault. If it hadn't been for him, I probably wouldn't have been watching Tiswas that Saturday morning and would never have even heard of Iron Maiden or their music. Okay, so Sally James might also have had something to do with me tuning into ITV's anarchic, anything goes answer to the BBC's far more sedate and well mannered Swap Shop as well, but that is almost certainly another conversation for another time.

So, there I was, diligently watching all manner of foam flying around the Tiswas studio and in the direction of the various minor celebrities who had agreed to be caged and humiliated in order to shill their latest whatever it was they were selling that week when it appeared on the screen in all its unfettered glory – *The Number of the Beast*. It was a revelation; I'd never seen anything like it before. The haunting introductory narration that I, at the time, assumed was Vincent Price* who had become my favourite actor after I'd been allowed to watch *Theatre of Blood* and *The Abominable Doctor Phibes* which then fed into a devastatingly catchy riff and haunting vocals immediately dug their claws into my imagination and refused to let go.

For four minutes and fifty something seconds I was transfixed and dumbfounded. Held in thrall by a group of musicians who were unlike anything I'd ever seen before who weren't singing about being in love with the girl next door or being cast aside in favour of a much better looking chap whose financial future was guaranteed and having their hearts broken in the process. My journey to the dark side was completed in less time than it takes to prepare a half decent hard boiled egg.

Before that video began, ten year old me spent his time immersed in the adventures of the Hardy Boys and Alfred Hitchcock's *Three Investigators*, reading 2000 AD and whatever Marvel Comics he could get his hands on, reliving the plots of *Star Wars* and *The Empire Strikes Back* with his ever expanding collection of Kenner and Palitoy figures and watching Tom Baker and Peter Davison travelling through time and space, battling the monster of the week. I hadn't given music much thought and apart from the odd disco number, Boney M** and the occasional Two-Tone tune that popped up on the radio, music didn't really play any part in my life. After it finished, my life was all about music; it became my everything.

I can't even pinpoint or single out what it was,

and is, about *The Number of the Beast* that touched my soul so deeply and profoundly. Maybe it was because it was about the devil and I'd just finished reading the novelisation of *The Omen* and Satan and all of his deliciously evil plans, machinations and schemes were weighing heavily on my mind. Maybe it appealed to me as I was a small, ginger child with a funny accent who loved all of the things that normal kids hated and immediately realised that this was the music of "outsiders", those "unfortunate" individuals who were either shunned by, or for some reason chose to live their lives on the fringes of, the mainstream and like always attracts, speaks to and reaches out for like. Or maybe it was just that ten year old me needed something to hold on to and Iron Maiden and heavy metal provided a tangible buoy that I could embrace and retreat to whenever I was being beaten like a garishly coloured piñata at a drunken student soiree for looking different, talking funny and not exactly being great at anything that involved physical activity.

Whatever it was, that song and that moment changed my life forever. It set in motion the chain of events that have shaped my existence. It's the reason that I started going to shows and gigs and was responsible for me failing my army physical***. It's why I spent too many wasted years**** playing in bands that never really went anywhere or did anything***** and ultimately why I became a journalist and later, a writer. Everything that I became, and am, is due to *The Number of the Beast* and Iron Maiden.

Blame Tiswas. I do.

Endnotes

*It isn't Vincent Price. It's a chap called Barry Clayton who was considerably cheaper, and asked for far less money, than Vincent Price.

** Boney M are vastly underrated. It's true and I'll argue that point with anyone who thinks otherwise. Because they're wrong.

*** I fractured my coccyx stage diving at a Napalm Death show when I was fifteen years old and as I was young, dumb and drunk at the time didn't realise what had happened until the next day. Cue five months of agony and a relatively short lived love affair with opiates and painkillers.

****It's an Iron Maiden in-joke. If you know the band and their music, you'll get it and if you don't... Well, never mind.

*****Mainly due to a lack of talent and the delusional belief that attitude and hard work were enough to "make it". They weren't, aren't and never will be.

46

Thirty-Seven Years of Lycanthrope Love

"A naked American man stole my balloons."

Backpacking and travelling around the world with nothing but the clothes on your back and the stuff in your rucksack used to be all the rage. This is almost certainly why Jack and David, two clean cut all-American youths and the main players in John Landis' tale of hirsute supernatural monstrosities find themselves rambling through the wind blasted moors of the North of England in the middle of winter. I don't know which tourist guide told them that this was the hip and happening pace to be in the early eighties, but whichever one it was should be ripped into pieces, set on fire and buried in a deep hole. Anyway, it starts to rain so they seek shelter in a local pub called The Slaughtered Lamb, which is a proper local watering hole for locals only and Landis makes this abundantly clear when the strangers walk in by ensuring that everyone in the crowded establishment shuts the fuck up as soon as they walk in and stare at the poor innocents abroad as though they were a posh red wine from somewhere like Tuscany. Which, anywhere north of Watford in the early eighties, was a big no-no and in some places was enough to get you run out of town.

Soon enough though, it's all laughs and banter as the teacher from *Kes*, Rick from *The Young Ones* and a whole host of other bit players accept their new comrades into their drinking club and all is going swimmingly until our clueless heroes start asking questions about the Pentagram on the wall, at which point they're kicked to the curb, thrown out in the rain and warned in no uncertain terms to stay off the moors. As they walk out of the pub and the locals' lives, there's a lot of hand wringing and chatter in the pub about how they shouldn't have let the lads leave while in the background there's a Lon Chaney style howl, which despite being louder than an old lady's telly, isn't heard by that bloke from Kes who obviously needs a hearing aid. Cut back to the young Americans chatting about girls and what not, who being young and out in the world for the first time, venture off the path and onto the moors. The opposite of they were told to do by the more local than local locals in the Slaughtered Lamb.

So, they're larking around when they hear something stalking them. Something big and growly, so they do what any semi-sensible folks would do in their place, put some speed in their feet and start to leg it. David falls over, Jack laughs about being scared and the whatever it is that was snarling at them (obviously a werewolf, because you know, the title of the film) leaps at Jack and starts ripping him to bits in the same way a drunk devours a kebab after ten pints. Cue David who's pissed off pretty sharpish because he doesn't want to end up like his chum but after a sudden attack of conscience turns around and heads back to help his friend, who, as David discovers, is now split from knackers to breakfast time and is all kinds of fucked up. Wolfie then turns his attention to David and gives him a bit of a kicking which he's only saved from by the reticent yokels turning up and blasting the crap out of hairy monster attacking him. David, lying on his back in the middle of a doubtless sheep shit filled field looks around at his assailant, who has returned to human form, then up at his saviours and promptly passes out.

Ten minutes. All of that happens in the first ten minutes of the film. There's no fannying around in *An American Werewolf in London*, no pointless exposition and not a single second wasted on chin stroking backstory or legend. It's all systems go from the off, which is probably why when I first saw it in 1982 with my great grandad, who hated everyone, was always half cut on whiskey and used to let his great-grandkids watch horror flicks with him just to wind our parents and his grand-kids up, it immediately struck a chord with me. Because I knew I wasn't supposed to be watching it, it got straight to the point without waffling on about any pointless crap, it's still the best were-wolf film ever made and its got Jenny Agutter in it. Oh wait, I haven't mentioned her yet have I? Okay, so David ends up in hospital, is interviewed by the police, is fed a line of bullshit about what hap-pened to him and we meet the square jawed Doc-tor Hirsch, who obviously is going to play a major part in whole scenario. But more importantly, there's Jenny Agutter. In a nurse's uniform. And she force feeds David. I know, right? It's like the best fantasy ever and every single time, without fail, that I think about that bit in the film, I get a warm fuzzy feeling in my gut and I can't help smiling. Too much information? Like I care. It's Jenny Agutter.

Anyways, David is visited by a spectral Jack who tells him about the whole curse of the werewolf thing and how he's in Limbo until the wolf's bloodline is ended and that can only happen when David is dead, so suggests the suicide route to stop his mate becoming all big, hairy and bitey. Even though David doesn't believe him, it's a nice touch, using the undead to castigate the living and give them spooky warnings and prophecies from beyond the grave. But the best thing about Jack is the seriously awesome, carved up zombie style make up that Griffin Dunne (the dude playing him) is smothered in. I mean, that shit looks seriously good now, and back in the eighties it was just the best. Seriously it was. Build yourself a time machine and go back and ask anyone who saw the film and they'll tell you exactly the same thing.

Even though David thinks he's going crazy and that Jack is full of shit, his dreams about hunting in the forest and Nazi demons ("Warmongers") stabbing Jenny Agutter after turning up at a family dinner to slay everyone in a hail of machine gun fire before slitting his throat, convince David that maybe something is amiss. The idea that David's subconscious is preparing his body and his conscious mind for what's about to happen to him via the medium of lucid dreaming is an interesting development in the film's narrative and adds depth to the character, but I maintain that the reason the dream scenes live long in the memories of everyone who ever seen the film is because as well as being incredibly inventive and original they're cooler than Tom Jones with a cocktail in hand, posing in his skimpiest briefs, surrounded by a bevy of naked ladies on the deck of a super yacht in nineteen seventy three. Which is why merchandise companies have sold the crap out of Warmonger figures for the last two and some spare change decades.

Oh, and while David's in the hospital, we're properly introduced to Jenny Agutter's character, Nurse Alex, via her rounds as she tends to sick children, emphasising the point that she's as nice as nice can be. While she's on her rounds, she stops off to talk to a boy who taught me a valuable life lesson, as every question she asks him, he answers by saying "No". That's life done properly, right there. Anytime that someone in a uniform asks you a question, you just say 'No". Trust me, it'll serve you well all the way down the line.

David then ends up back at Alex's flat because he's an American and obviously has nowhere else to stay (has nobody heard of youth hostels?) and before you can say "Ding Dong" they're both in the nip and going for it like there's no tomorrow. I mean, I don't blame David, because it's Jenny Agutter and you would, wouldn't you? Thing is, and this is the only bit of the film that gets on my tits, during the whole how's your father scene, Van Morrison's *Moon Dance* is playing in the background, when the song that they should have used is Warren Zevon's *Werewolves of London*, because Warren was infinitely more refined and swish than Van and I've always thought that Morrison was a little creepy. In an "investigated by Operation Yewtree because he drives an ice cream van and hangs out in the blackest recesses of the dark web" kind of way.

Jack reappears, he looks more wonderfully horrible than ever, warns David again, David tells him he looks like the kind of thing that the typical American family would eat for dinner and Alex struts around the place looking magnificent before heading back to work and leaving David in her flat alone to root through her underwear drawer and eat everything in the fridge. Okay, so I made that last bit up, because he just watches one of the three telly channels that we had when this film was made. Mind you, I'd almost certainly have eaten everything in the fridge. And given the chance, I'd probably have had a rummage through Jenny Agutter's underwear drawer too.

Remember the square jawed doctor? Well, while Alex was working her way through the Karma Sutra with David, and Jack was probably perving on them from inside the cupboard, the doctor decided to visit East Proctor (where the Slaughtered Lamb was) in order to find out more about the decidedly fishy circumstances under which David arrived in his care. Having been told that his patient was assaulted by a lunatic, but unable to find any witnesses or corroborative evidence and being able to smell horseshit a mile away, he sets off to have a bit of a poke around and investigate for himself. He also drives an MG. And drinks Guinness. Of course he does. I'll bet he smoked a pipe and had a velvet robe that he liked to wear when entertaining his special ladies as well. So he does the questioning thing, and his hackles are put out of joint and one of the locals ends up confessing to him in a moment of supplication in which the hard drinking Northern bloke who isn't afraid of werewolves, goes all trembly at the knees when the chap from the South turns up and starts asking a few questions. It's probably an allegory for the class struggle and the social and economic divide that still separates England into two distinctively different countries, but before the point can really be hammered home and the Northern bloke can doff his cap, the chap from *Kes* shows up and puts a halt to proceedings by shouting a lot and no doubt silently communicating to his drinking comrade that if he talks anymore, he'll spend the rest of the day in a figure four leg lock. Because the bloke from *Kes*, more commonly known as Brian Glover, used to wrestle on *World of Sport* and was dead good at it. Honest, he really did, have a look on YouTube and the like and watch him handing out some serious seventies style smack downs.

So, now the doctor is speeding back to London to see what Alex, who's in work, knows about David. Meanwhile, David's in the flat and the fact that Creedence Clearwater Revival's *Bad Moon Rising* is playing while Dave reads his book means that something serious is about to happen, and boy oh boy, soon as that tune finishes it kicks off like a roider on a Friday night coke binge. We were promised a werewolf and I'll be damned if we don't get the finest lunar dependent monster to have ever been committed to film that appears following a transformation sequence that made effects guru Rick Baker famous the world over. It's a bone stretching and snapping scene that immediately conveys how painful it is for one creature to morph into another, while projecting the shock, terror and fear that overwhelms David as the curse takes hold. It still looks incredible and is, for me at least, one of the defining moments of onscreen horror. And yes, it's still funny watching him nearly burst into werewolf tears as he watches his ding-a-ling disappear.

While Doctor Hirsch and Alex ham it up in a frantic attempt to enforce just how worried they are about David after failing to contact him, he sets out on his first night of murder and mayhem, chowing down on a couple off to a fondue and goodness knows what else dinner party, a trio of tramps and an uptight, middle management type whose train arrived a few minutes too late to save his life. The latter is the reason that the tube still freaks me out as I can't venture underground to ride the rails in London without imagining that I'm going to be stalked by some slavering beast who'll then consume me on a rickety, past its prime escalator. Bloody Landis, it's all his fault that the Victoria Line still gives me the chills. Oh, and in the background? There's the first reference in *An American Werewolf* to John Landis' favourite cinematic joke, one that he reuses in a number of his films, this time appearing as a film poster on the wall of the station as the hapless victim is chased to his death. That's right kids; it's *See You Next Wednesday.*

After eating his fill of Londoners, David wakes up in the zoo's lupine enclosure, which just goes to show that the old adage about lying down with dogs is probably true. Except this time, it's wolves. In the buff and alone, David steals a coat and some private school kid's balloons, which is still one of my favourite gags of all time and despite having been to the US of A on a number of occasions and having spent a lot of time around its citizens, I'm yet to stumble across a situation where I've been able to use it, but one day, oh yes one day when the stars align and the time is right, I'll find myself in some impossibly fucked up encounter where I can exclaim to everyone and no one in particular "A naked American man stole my balloons".

Clueless about what he's done, David meets up with Alex and on her insistence accompanies her to see Doctor Hirsch. They don't reach their destination as while riding in a taxi driven by Bricktop from *Snatch*, the hapless cabbie tells them all about the previous night's grizzly murders and David, realising the truth, flees the cab and Alex, and after failing to get himself arrested, holes up in a porno cinema with Jack and the departed spirits of his victims. All of whom insist on admonishing him and suggesting ways in which he can do away with himself. Thing is though, his victims are awfully "British" about being used as chew toys and are insufferably polite despite having been murdered in a most gruesome fashion, which I know is all about finding humour in the most awful of situations, but not one of them questions their killer's parentage or accuses him of dallying with his mother, which I'm pretty sure is something that most of us would do. But then I suppose seeing Linzi Drew half naked in *See You Next Wednesday*, which is the feature playing in the filth palace that David has chosen to hide out in, and the second and last use in the film of Landis' favourite gag, is enough to calm anyone's nerves and ensure goodwill to all men and monsters – even the one who's just eaten all of your best bits in an orgy of explicitly brutal violence.

Like all good things though, and in homage to all of the best Universal Horror films of the thirties and forties which were all about the build-up before crashing to a brief, but gloriously detailed finale, the end is nigh as David does his full moon lupine bit again and the Werewolf's second, and last, outing sees him eating the other perverts in the fleapit before wreaking havoc in Leicester Square. Heads roll, buses crash and lots of people meet their makers in many dreadful and frightfully imaginative ways. Following a rather impressive body count, and having been cornered by the heavily armed Fuzz, Alex and Doctor Hirsch rush to the scene to try and "talk" to David, who after Alex tells him she loves him shows her his best gummy smile before he's gunned down by the Po-Po. And all that's left as The Marcels launch into *Blue Moon* and the credits begin to roll, is a naked American man with no balloons lying in a filthy London alleyway, surrounded by strangers and a wailing Jenny Agutter. What a way to go. Beware the moon...

*I know that *Werewolf* was released in 1981, which means it's thirty-eight years old, but I didn't see it until 1982. So, there you go. Thirty-seven years.

47

Cause For Alarm

Nineteen eighty-six was the year that changed everything. The New Wave of British Heavy Metal, or NWOBHM (try saying that with a gobstopper in your mouth) had risen, conquered the world and fallen, slayed by the spandex wearing, big hair having, make up clad rock warriors of the Sunset Strip and their disciples who had in turn fallen to the chugga-chugga riffs of the hyper velocity, furious upstart metal assault that had found a base in the Bay Area of San Francisco and Oakland.

Thrash had arrived and its surprisingly quick, and ruthless, takeover of the minds of denim and leather clad devotes from Brazil to Basingstoke was spearheaded by the cultural phenomenon that was Metallica's third album, *Master of Puppets*. While most die hard thrashers would argue that it was actually *Reign in Blood*, Slayer's tertiary opus that forever changed the face of metal, *Master* was released six months before *Blood* and opened the floodgates that allowed the masses to begin obsessing over what, had up to that point, been a relatively small, closed off and members' only sub-genre of metal.

Like most of my brothers in metal, I was bewitched and entranced by thrash. Its raw fury, aggression and channelled energy spoke to me unlike anything else had before. The music was a reflection of everything that I was feeling; it touched my soul and made my every atom and fibre of my being tingle with excitement and electricity. Nothing else could compare to the devastating power of thrash. I was a thrasher and I'd determined that was what I was going to be until I find solace and peace in the comfort of the grave. And I'd probably still be a thrash obsessive if it hadn't been for a largely unknown, and mostly unheard of, band called Agnostic Front.

Released in the intervening period between Metallica and Slayer's career defining moments, *Cause for Alarm* was Agnostic Front's second album and their first for an international label, Combat which along with its parent Relativity was later subsumed by Sony. The music business, even the independent music business, is a vicious beast that will happily, and without conscience, consume any part of itself if it thinks it will be of benefit or generate profit. Where was I? That's right, *Cause for Alarm*.

It was a late summer evening, sometime toward the end of August and I was hanging out with my friend Mark after I'd spent a thoroughly satisfying day being young and dumb. There may well have been illicit alcohol and cigarettes involved, there usually was, some of the details have become a little hazy and have faded with time. As we sat there listening to the usual bunch of metal mal-contents growl and scream about the Seven Churches, Mark pulled a record out of his collec-tion, grinned and said:

"You have to hear this..."

He slipped the record out of its sleeve, put it on his stereo, dropped the needle and handed me the cover. As the initial crackle of the needle finding the grooves began, I stared at the artwork on the album's cover. It was a brutal, cartoonsh confla-gration of demonic skinheads, obese businessmen and punks being preyed upon by outlandish thugs that while being entirely in keeping with the vast majority of my record collection, still took me by surprise as it steered clear of the usual dark brooding, fantasy and horror heavy imagery I was used too. While all of the characters that adorned the sleeve were heavily exaggerated caricatures, the imagery was rooted in reality, not one that I was familiar with, but reality nonetheless. I flipped it over and stared at the stark, black and white image of the band on the back. Taken against the backdrop of a bleak building some-where on the Lower East Side of New York, it was unlike any band photograph that I'd ever seen. They weren't posing for the camera, or gurning and contorting their faces into all sorts of strange "Look-at-me-I'm-far-more- metal-than-you" faces in an attempt to look crazy and slightly out of step with the rest of society, they just stood there*, relaxed, staring out at the world. They looked like the meanest bunch of mother-fuckers** ever, like they'd rather carve you into little pieces and feed you to the mythical alligators that supposedly lived in the sewers under their city instead of greeting you with a pleasant 'How do you do' and sharing banal anecdotes about the weather. And then the music started and something deep inside my brain exploded with the force of ten megaton bomb.

This was thrash taken to the nth degree, stripped of all of its pomposity and needlessly technical fare. It was fast, furious and burning with a righteous anger that was hammered home with every syllable of the rabid vocals, machine gun rhythms and deliriously catchy riffs that swirled around, repeating endlessly, in my head. From the opening salvo of *The Eliminator* to the closing barrage of *Shoot His Load*, *Cause for Alarm* was, musically, everything that I didn't know I'd been looking for. In what seemed like an instant, but was actually more like twenty-five minutes, it became my favourite album. *Cause for Alarm* was the first hardcore record I ever heard and Agnostic Front began my life long, love affair with both the New York and global hardcore scenes. Their music encouraged me to step out of the metal scene and to immerse myself in the punk underground, a scene that nearly thirty-three years later, I'm still a part of.

I'm a hardcore kid, I always have been and I always will be. And it's all thanks to Agnostic Front.

Endnotes

*Apart from Roger (Miret), AF's vocalist, who's reclining against a wall while sitting on top of what looks like some sort of refuse container.

** They're not. I've met, and interviewed, Vinnie (Stigma – guitar) and Roger on a number of occasions and they're absolute sweethearts. They're two of the friendliest, most open and down to Earth chaps it's been my privilege to cross paths with. And Vinnie is one of life's genuine eccentrics who makes the most of, and enjoys, every second. But I still wouldn't cross either of them, because you never know...

48

Now there comes a time...

"Now there comes a time for a man to walk away..."

When do you know that enough is enough? That something is over, a chapter of your life is coming to an end and that it's time to let go and move on? When do you know that the end is nigh? For me, it happened on a Sunday evening in May, when I'd normally have been stuck in band practice, drenched in sweat, screaming into a microphone while being deafened by a wall of incredibly fast hardcore noise. But this particular Sunday, for some real life, adult reason that I've since forgotten, I wasn't trapped in the sweat lodge running through the band's set list at Mach 10. There was no practice and I was making the most of it.

The days were getting longer and the sun's heat was gradually diminishing; I was savouring a bottle of Jones Soda while watching *The Legacy of Arrow Development* and it suddenly hit me. I didn't want to do it anymore. I was happy where I was, doing what I was doing and my days of playing punk rock were over. And at that moment, I real-

315

ised that I was completely and totally, forever and ever amen, done with the band thing.

According to tenets of long held wisdom, the truth will set you free and the truth was that I just wasn't enjoying playing punk rock. My heart wasn't it, I'd lost my focus, forgotten why I'd thought it would be fun to go back and do it all over again after a double decade hiatus and the reasons I was doing it, from a personal perspective, had become increasingly blurred. Originally, I'd wanted to play hardcore again simply to prove that I still could. That I had enough gas left in my tank to take one more swing at it before stepping off the stage and turning the amplifiers off for good.

And I'd made myself, and Gav who I formed AxTxOxTx (otherwise known as All Time Old Time) with, a promise before we even started to seriously think about it. We'd do it for twelve months, record some songs, play some shows and then get the heck out of Hardcore Town before most folks even knew we'd arrived. It had, at the time, seemed like a good plan.

The thing with plans though is that they change. They don't mean to, they just do. Blame it on whatever you like, circumstance, fate, the divergent destinies of the souls involved or just the way things happen to pan out on any given Sunday, the rules that govern such things are malleable and as such, even the best laid plans of

316

punks and men swiftly disappear down unfore-seen rabbit holes almost as soon as they're, well, you know, planned.

The first mistake I made was writing a set of lyrics that were directed at a specific individual and his behaviour; words that highlighted what I and others saw as the rank hypocrisy of someone who'd elevated himself to a self-elected position of "power" and had adopted, and started living by the mantra, "Do what I say, not what I do".

At first, I thought it was sort of funny, that I was just poking the bear and that maybe he'd see it the same way and laugh at the ridiculousness of the whole thing with me and the rest of the band. But he didn't. And when face to face at a show we played, I sang/screamed/shouted the words straight at him, I saw something in his eyes that I'll never forget. Hurt. It had never even occurred to me that by writing those lyrics, I'd tried to force my ideas on someone else through mockery and by belittling the choices and decisions that they'd made. There's a word for that kind of behaviour, it's called bullying. For the sake of a cheap pop and an easy laugh, I'd become a bully and after being gut punched by that realisation, every single time I sang that song, live or in practice, a little part of my soul died because I knew I'd become one of the things that I loathed most in the world. The worst thing about it though, was that I lost a friend. He blamed me for that song. And you know what? He was right. It was my fault. I'm sorry.

My second mistake was not taking the passage of time into account and adjusting to it accordingly. The last time I'd fronted a band, I was in my early twenties and I'd been able to jump around, bounce up and down and take a kicking and keep on ticking. But that was then and this was now, and the intervening years had, physically at least, not been kind. Middle aged spread and old injuries that were mostly the result of a misspent youth had finally caught up with me and didn't just gently nag me anymore; they screamed, shouted and cajoled me at every, and any, given chance. And while I had Devon Morf and Ray Cappo inspired visions of flying through the sky like some aerial superhero and interacting with the audience, in actuality I could maybe get a foot or so off the ground at best and large groups of people are not exactly my forte, which made any sort of interaction with the folks who came to see us somewhat difficult. Although, given the number of people who actually came to our shows or turned out to see us, I really shouldn't have worried about the crowd thing. It was never a problem.

My third mistake was the worst though. I forgot about Ohana. I let the band come before my family. One of the last shows that we played, an afternoon matinee was on the same day as a cheer competition that my daughter was competing in. I chose to play the show and I hated every second of it. I knew I shouldn't have been there, I knew I should have been perched on cramped, plastic seating in an arena that had seen better days applauding my daughter and her friends and cheering them on to victory instead of playing fast songs about rollercoasters, Dungeons & Dragons and Ric Flair to the usual miscreants and a smattering of strangers. Ohana means family. Ohana means that nobody gets left behind. And that day, I left myself and my daughter behind to try and prove a self-indulgent, way past its sell by date point. I swore I would never let that happen again. It was the beginning of the end. I just hadn't realised it.

Three really is a magic number, as it was the culmination of those factors (and a multitude of other less important things) that on a Sunday in late May while watching a documentary about the company who helped build Disneyland, made me realise that my days of playing punk rock had, at long last, come to a close. So, I hung up my microphone, turned off the stage lights and walked away. It was both the hardest, and easiest, decision that I've ever made. And I've never been happier.

49

Four Buck Chuck – The Dystopian King of Alternative Futures

Joe Strummer believed that the future is unwritten. That it was up to each of us to make of it what we will and that the only thing preventing humanity from reaching a golden age of unlimited possibility and potential was our inclination toward self-destruction and inability to overcome our base biological drives. The former frontman of the Clash was a dreamer who dared to believe in hope and had faith in the notion that people, when you get right down to the meat and gristle of it, will always do the right thing and are, despite overwhelming evidence to the contrary, inherently good. Which is kind of an odd philosophy to adhere to given that he grew up in the sixties and early seventies, a period defined by political assassination and revolution, the cold war, the Vietnam conflict, the Cuban missile crisis, upheaval in the Middle East and the near constant threat of nuclear annihilation. Even the most rabidly optimistic vehicles that emerged during that era, the Civil Rights movement, Doctor Who, Star Trek, the youthful superpowered heroes created by Stan Lee, Steve Ditko and Jack Kirby, the hippies, the yippies and the counter culture ensemble and the rapidly evolving punk tsunami that was born in the sweatbox clubs of New York's Lower East Side were not enough to stem the growth of the time's aura of pervasive doom. And so, its blackened tentacles slowly, but surely, snaked their way into every avenue, both the fantastic and mundane alike, of life.

While apocalyptic antiutopian science fiction was nothing new and can be traced back to the populist beginning of the genre via the novels of HG Wells and Jules Verne, most famously *The War of the Worlds*, *Twenty Thousand Leagues Under the Sea* and *The Time Machine*, it was during the nineteen sixties that its roots firmly buried themselves in the literary, and later cinematic, form. It was the sixties that saw the emergence of space opera on the world stage, as the global bestseller *Dune* – the story of a bleak far flung future dominated by feudalism and totalitarian rule – led the market and the anti-hero, best characterised by Jim DiGriz, Harry Harrison's *Stainless Steel Rat*, became the norm rather than a rarity. The exceptions to the rule, that space was a dangerous and unforgiving place and the future held nothing but limitless misery, took precedence over fables that were filled with dreams of an impossible paradise as genre fiction began to mirror the world in which its creators lived. And as the literature that formed the backbone of the genre became darker, so did its usually lighter hearted, cinematic cousin. Hollywood took the new nihilistic outlook of science fiction to heart and found an unlikely champion to spearhead its brief, but incredibly successful, dalliance with the dark side.

By the time he was cast in *Planet of the Apes*, Charlton Heston had already parted the Red Sea, met Jesus, gunned Nazi fighter aircraft out of the sky and driven a chariot faster than any other man alive. He hadn't though, until donning George Taylor's astronaut outfit, had a major box office hit for nearly a decade, but was still seen as a safe pair of hands and a bankable name to headline Franklin Schaffner's radically different adaptation of Pierre Boulle's novel of a post-apocalyptic future ruled by primates. It was the first act in Chuck's dystopian quartet, and while, half a century after it was first released, it still has an element of shock value, the film's major revelations and big reveals have become part of the popular zeitgeist; and there isn't a geek worth her or his salt out there who can't quote Chucks dirty paws speech verbatim and who isn't more than familiar with the Statue of Liberty ending. Seen as a righteous social critique and condemnation of segregation and endorsement of ending the woefully ridiculous policy of mutually assured destruction that the Russian and US governments had become locked into, *Planet of the Apes* also put the man who would be Taylor back on the map, made him a big money action star and set him on course to become the King of Dystopia. The fact that it drew an audience who didn't know the difference between Arthur C Clarke and Robert Heinlein, and returned nearly seven times its budget at the box office made the silver screen men who pulled the levers behind the Hollywood curtain sit up and take notice. Subscribing to the joint philosophies of striking while the iron was hot and that if something isn't broken then it doesn't need fixing, the fiduciary giants who gave the thumbs up to all things film related wanted more ape and Taylor action and so a sequel, *Beneath the Planet of the Apes*, was ordered and rushed into production.

On May 26 1970, twenty-five months after they first ventured through that strange time aberration with George Taylor and his doomed crew, audiences were invited to return to the terrifying monkey dominated future in the company of Brent, the only survivor of a mission sent to discover what happened to Taylor and his shipmates. The emphasis this time around is on Brent (played by James Franciscus) a medallion ready hirsute man's man, cut from the same acting cloth as Chuck, and his descent into near madness as he desperately searches for Taylor and is forced to accept the truth of where he really is a full half hour or so before his predecessor did in the first film. Realising that no matter how good *Planet of the Apes* was, you can't make the same film twice and expect audiences to fall in love with it all over again unless you're JJ Abrams, writer Paul Dehn and director Ted Post decided to mix things up a little with *Beneath the Planet of the Apes* and introduced a cult of bomb worshipping mutants to add a little zip, and a whole load of crazy, to the plot.

Which brings us back to Taylor, whose role in the sequel is reduced to an extended, but essential, cameo and whom, Brent and the audience both discover, has become a prisoner of the aforementioned pseudo-technocratic religious maniacs. Pitting the "muties" against the monkeys was a clumsy allegory that was supposed to represent the ongoing cold war between the, at the time, two global superpowers and the cult's glorification of atomic weaponry bluntly reinforces the notion that the first film hammered home; that nukes are like really, really bad. While the opposing forces duke it out, and having taken care of Brent in a hail of bullets that emphasises just how cheap life has become in the "future", it is left up to Taylor to have the final word, which he does in grand fashion. With his dying breath, King Chuck proves that he's the most important man on that damn dirty planet and the last hero that any of the mutants and monkeys will ever know, by pushing, while cursing and damning everyone to hell, the big button and putting paid to the whole sorry state of affairs once and for all. Charlton Heston in his final moments as Taylor becomes the man who killed the world.

The downbeat ending of *Beneath the Planet of the Apes* left a slightly sour, depressing taste in the minds of mainstream film fans and word of mouth and reviews ensured that cinema audiences showed their displeasure in the only way they knew how: by staying away. And even though the sequel made far less than the original, the Apes' franchise survived for another three years and three more films before the idea of Apetopia was eventually retired. This made absolutely no difference to Chuck's career though, as he was already dead in the franchise, having blown up, and thus put paid to, the unforgiving and sombre world which he'd ended up in. So, it was time for him to move on. And move on he did to even more barbarous, austere and ominous fictional futures.

The first step on the road to those futures was *The Omega Man*. It was the second time that Hollywood had tried to film Richard Matheson's stygian novel of survival in a world ravaged by a vampiric plague, *I Am Legend* and *The Omega Man* attempted to do what the previous cinematic version, the Vincent Price led *The Last Man on Earth*, hadn't − strike it big at the box office. As

Heston was still relatively fresh with an all-ages audience following the success of his simian led features, putting him in the driving seat as the film's protagonist, Robert Neville, seemed like a no-brainer. After all, he'd hit a home run and charged in at the last moment to save the game with both of the monkey movies he'd been in, so logic dictated that he must have been doing something right. And logic, as it ever is, was absolutely right when it came to Chuck assuming the mantle of Robert Neville. While it didn't make as much money as the producers, director and studio would have liked or wanted, *The Omega Man* is a harsh and uncompromising film and its plot was led by the prevailing climate in which it was made. Neville, a former US Army scientist and the "saviour" of humanity, developed the serum to the war-born, and created, virus which has destroyed mankind and carries the only sample of it in his blood. Hounded throughout the film by the Family, a cult like group of plague victims who have been mutated by the pathogen that he holds the answer to, Neville rediscovers hope when he stumbles across a group of young people who he, with a little help, can immunise and send out into the world to start all over again.

But this is a Chuck film and his take on science fiction offers little reward for the characters he plays, and as such for Neville to give humanity another chance, he has to die. Which he does, giving his blood to his "disciples" so that they might live. The last half of *The Omega Man* is steeped in religious symbolism, with Neville, and thus Chuck, becoming a Christ like figure as he leads a group of young people to salvation despite the protestations and best attempts of the masses, portrayed in this instance, by The Family. Neville even dies in a Jesus Christ pose in the fountain in front his house, having been run through by a spear, and the final shot of the film's "crucified" martyr leaves the audience in no doubt that when push came to shove, even though he was part of the establishment that did its best to kill every man and woman on the planet, in the end he wasn't such a bad chap after all. In fact, you might even call him a "hero". It's also sort of fitting that, having previously met Christ earlier in his career when he played Ben Hur, Chuck finally got to "be" the Messiah. Or at least a not so heavily disguised, drowned in metaphor version of him anyway. And even though this was the second time in a science fiction row that Chuck "died", when he ventures into the great beyond in *The Omega Man*, he saves the world instead of blowing it up.

Most thespians would have been more than happy to venture into humanity's desolate history yet to come three times. Chuck wasn't most people though and in 1973 he teamed up with the producer of *The Omega Man*, Walter Seltzer, again to paint one last cinematic portrait of a ruined society in which humanity had fallen victim to corporate greed and hubris. *Soylent Green*, based on a short story by Harry Harrison, is scarily prophetic and bears an uncannily resemblance to the scientifically predicted not so distant future that humanity is actually heading for. Set in an ecologically damaged and vastly overpopulated 2022, Chuck plays an NYPD detective who while investigating a homicide stumbles across a terrible truth that's been hidden behind conspiracy and high power double dealing. That the Soylent Corporation has been processing the dead and repurposing them as food, the Soylent Green of the title, to feed an ever expanding population that has increased far beyond the world's natural ability to provide for it.

Rather than subject its anti-hero, Detective Frank Thorn, to the sort of digitised, mass info-dump that's increasingly commonplace in the twenty first century, *Soylent Green*, sticking rigidly to the grand seventies conspiracy thriller rule-book, gradually drip feeds its central player clues that hint at, and point toward, the inevitable conclusion. That *Soylent Green* is people. And director Richard Fleischer and one-man sci-fi wrecking ball Chuck needle the film's message home through an ensemble of set pieces. The rivalry that's set up between Chuck Connors and Chuck Heston, allows the two Chucks in their finest fashionable threads and nattiest of caps to battle it out throughout the film in their good versus evil guises, culminating in a bitter sweet, and almost ambiguous victory for Good Chuck. The brutal riot scenes and the procession of characters who are willing to do whatever it takes to taste the easy life and rise above the masses, all serve to point out that this future, this dystopian hell, is one of our own making. It's also Chuck's finest on-screen sci-fi performance, as the journey Frank undertakes as he transforms from someone who readily subscribes to the "me first" philosophy that dominates the lives of the populace he's sworn to protect, into an individual whose job becomes the centre of his existence and for whom the truth is more important than his own existence, is made all too believable by the daily misery and sorrow, interspersed with a few moments of true joy, that he faces on a daily basis. And it's this film, this role and the dying moments of the story in which Frank's and the Soylent Corporation's intertwined fates remain uncertain as the credits begin to roll, that inexorably crowns Charlton 'Chuck' Heston as the King of Dystopia.

In the decades that followed the release of *Soylent Green*, Chuck's box office power would slowly begin to dissipate with *Earthquake* being his last marquee headlining draw to make any sort of serious financial and critical impact. And while he continued to make films, his name moved further and further down the cast list and Charlton Heston slipped into the comfortable and unassuming role of Hollywood royalty. No matter what else he did in later life though, his shifting political allegiance, a waning career dominated by bad choices – ultimately only saved by *True Lies* and *In the Mouth of Madness* – and a bizarre devotion to the ridiculous psycho-babble of the NRA, thanks to his spirted and memorable performances in the quartet of films that helped to define the cinematic vision of unfolding dystopian societies for decades to come, Charlton Heston will always be the King of Uncertain Futures. The king is dead, long live the king.

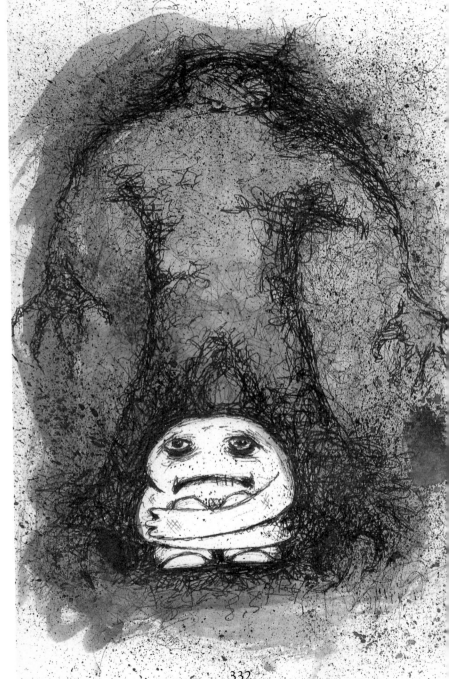

50

Anger Is An Energy

For most of my life, anger has been my constant companion. Not the type of humdrum, everyday, here one minute and gone the next anger that misplacing your keys, stubbing your toe or spilling your coffee causes to rise, fuel an expletive or two and then fall away to nothing almost as quickly as it appeared. Nope, that shit was like breakfast cereal for me, I'd eat a couple of bowls of it in the morning and then get ready for the day's main event to boil and bubble away in every atom of my being; and then, and only then, would I feel ready to face the world.

That anger came from somewhere. There was a cause and then there was the effect; the action and reaction. The thing is though, there isn't a single event that I can categorically and unequivocally isolate and state: "Yeah, this is where it comes from, this is the root cause of all if it". Whatever the original cause, my response to any trigger was always the same. Anger. I opened the cage and freed my monster, the creature that I fed and nurtured and allowed to damn near consume my life.

Thing is, it's easy to blame circumstance. The whole A led to B led to C, that's why I'm angry, that's why the red mist descends and that's why I battered that bloke and tried to make a necklace out of his teeth. But blaming whatever it was, and is, that started feeding the beast and kept its belly full is just a cheap way of absolving responsibility and taking the easy route out of Accountability City, which allowed me to shrug my shoulders and mutter "It's just the way I am, it's not my fault" for nearly four decades. At some point you have to step back, peak behind the curtain, take control of all the levers, switches and ridiculously complicated arrays of buttons and figure out how, and why, the machine works.

And it isn't easy. Digging up and dusting off all of the crap that you've buried down deep, confronting it head on and trying to find a way to deal with it isn't exactly a Sunday afternoon stroll in the park. For instance, the fact that I was bullied incessantly for nearly ten years because I was a slight, ginger kid who liked (and still likes) "weird" stuff like comics, Dungeons & Dragons, science fiction and preferred, horror of all horrors, to read books instead of mindlessly smashing other people's property was a pretty bitter pill to taste, let alone swallow, and dwelling on it always launched me headlong down the fast track to Furyville.

Accepting that I spent day after day as a verbal and physical punching bag for most of my peers simply because I was smaller and weaker than them and understanding that it was simplistic, tribal behaviour made manifest and nothing more was tough to deal with. Knowing that the morons who bullied me were simply following primitive biological instincts didn't make it any easier and didn't change the fact that they were, and almost certainly still are, profoundly stupid and lacking in any sort of imagination, individuality or per-sonality. It did allow me to understand why it happened and knowing the why, allowed me to give it context, examine it from a different per-spective and after days of soul searching, let go of all the pain, misery and the twisted, strange fucked up belief that maybe I was to blame for what happened to me. I wasn't. I never was. The kids who bullied me, they were responsible for their own actions, just like I'm responsible for mine, and the way that I reacted to and didn't deal with the situation. They were responsible for what they did, it wasn't my fault.

It also wasn't my fault that an overtly touchy feely leader of a well known youth organisation, which I was a member of as a child, took it upon himself to play the role of a real life Uncle Ernie and have a jolly fine old time fiddling about with adolescent me. I buried the memory of that encounter deep in the blackest, darkest corner of my mind and left it there to fester, rot and allowed its slow decay to feed the demon that had buried its claws deep in my soul rather than letting it out of its prison. Maybe if I had, maybe if I hadn't been too scared to face it, I'd have also freed myself. But I didn't. I kept it a secret, just like I'd been told to and I let it feed my monster. I know it wasn't my fault, and I knew it wasn't my fault at the time, but fear is a great motivator and while it's changed its face many times since it first sank its fangs into me, that fear was always present. It was always there and that's why it stayed, remaining camouflaged and suckling the devil that I did know until I finally exposed it and let it burn in the cold, hard light of that day. It was a terrible thing that happened to me, but I've now learned to deal with it in my own way and accept it. It might not be the healthiest coping strategy, but in some twisted, defective way it works for me and right here, right now, that'll have to do.

Then there's every fucked up relationship, every betrayal, every promise broken, every opportunity that I was too afraid to take because I'd been stripped of any, and all, self-confidence and never thought I was good enough to deserve, or amount to, anything, and the thought of those countless roads not travelled because fate had stripped me of any mettle that I once had, it burned. And as it burned it fed my anger, its constant flame heating that fury to boiling point, maintaining it so that it was always ready to spill over at any moment and scorch anyone and everyone who ever crossed my path.

But that was then, and this is now. This is the now when I've pulled all of that shit up, embraced and accepted it and allowed it to become a part of me instead of defining me and I'm no longer a slave to my monster. I control it, it doesn't control me. But just because I've come to terms with the fires that fuelled my fury, it doesn't mean that I've forgiven or forgotten the pyromaniacs who started the conflagration, I haven't. I'm not that kind of man. Not yet. I might be one day, but at the moment, acceptance is all I've got, it's the best that I can do and my best is just going to have to be good enough. One day I might find a better way. But until I do, it's all I've got.

Don't get me wrong. I still get angry. I still feel that bubbling, boiling, burning rage surging through my every fibre. It's still a part of me. It probably always will be. But acceptance has taught me that I can live in harmony with my rage and that I don't have to let it out unless I want to. I control my anger, it doesn't control me. And right now, that'll do. That'll do just fine.

51

Nine Hundred And Ninety-Nine Happy Haunts And The Frankenstein Place

On the 12 of August 1969, the attraction that been a long held dream of Walt Disney, and for the previous half decade the subject of idle guest speculation and half whispered urban legend, finally opened its doors. As visitors enthusiastically climbed aboard the Doombuggies which took them on a guided tour of its uncanny corridors and introduced them to its spectral residents, the Haunted Mansion, as well as shattering Disneyland attendance records during its inaugural week, seemingly took on a life of its own and began to transcend its somewhat humble origins.

Eager to capitalise on its burgeoning popularity, Disneyland Records released *The Story and Song from the Haunted Mansion* which told the tale of the benighted house and its residents and gave prospective riders an overview of what to expect when they eventually visited the cobwebbed corridors of New Orleans Square's ghost riddled dwelling. Featuring a cast that included Ron Howard, Robie Lester, Thurl Ravenscroft, Pete

Renoudet and Eleanor Audley as well as the song that continuously echoes through the grounds of the Haunted Mansion's mist shrouded graveyard, the album became a cult classic among aficionados and devotees of Disney's haunted house.

Meanwhile, four years later and half a world away in London, a budding young actor by the name of Richard O'Brien was preparing to unleash his musical endeavour on an unsuspecting and, truth be told, somewhat naive public. Having devoted himself to its creation, O'Brien was at last ready to let the proletariat sample the production that would change the lives of thousands by encouraging them to embrace freedom and personal liberation in a manner they had hadn't dared to dream was possible.

The Rocky Horror Show made its theatrical debut at the Royal Court Theatre in London on the 19th of June, 1973 and the rest, ladies and gentlemen, is history. It immediately found its audience among the post-hippie generation who revelled in the show's celebration of kitsch science fiction and horror, sexual adventure and the loss and abandonment of innocence that played out against a backdrop of bawdy innuendo, infectious songs and knowing reverential humour. Within two years it had made its cinematic debut and since its opening night, the film and the show have played almost non-stop on stage and screen

around the globe. It became a cultural phenomenon and monster that its creator, much like Mary
Shelley, whose most famous novel it liberally bor-
rows from, could never, even in his wildest
imaginings, have foreseen.

Separated by time and space, these two seemingly unconnected paragons of fringe culture
have, during the last half century, played a key
role in helping to shape the face of fandom. But
perhaps the gulf that divides them isn't quite as
wide as it first appears. Maybe the Haunted Mansion, or at least the story that has helped to
encourage generations to visit it, and *The Rocky
Horror Show* continue to thrive thanks to a handful
of expertly utilised, and incorporated, genre
tropes. And maybe, just maybe, the narratives that
drive and sustain them aren't so different after all.

From the beginning, audiences are taken firmly
by the hand and deftly manoeuvred through each
act of both stories by a narrator whose rich, bass-
heavy voice engenders a sense of immediate familiarity despite their ominous settings and the
lurking danger that threatens to engulf the proceedings at any moment. This guiding presence
that both stories rely on allows the spectators to
totally submerge themselves in the respective
dramas and become passive observers instead of
active participants content in the knowledge that
their guide, having at least some idea of what is to

come, won't allow the fate that awaits the players to befall the wards placed in his charge.

The Story and Song... and *The Rocky Horror Show* both feature, as their protagonists, a teenage couple, who having been caught in that most glorious of old horror movie clichés, the thunder-storm, seek shelter from the inclement weather in a fortuitously available, dark and foreboding manor house; or castle as said refuge presents itself in *The Rocky Horror Picture Show*. Once they cross the thresholds of the respective mansions, each couple embarks on an adventure that will forever alter their lives and the way they relate to, and see, the world.

Draw deeper into their individual scenarios, the characters are exposed to the whims and fancies of the inhabitants of the decadent palaces in which they are, temporarily at least, trapped. Mike and Karen, the avatars the Haunted Mansion uses to tell its legend, are protected by the Ghost Host, the former lord of the manor who tells them that he won't allow any harm to come to them provid-ing they accompany him on a tour of his home and let him introduce them to the residents.

Serving the dual purpose of creating a definitive mythology and generating a sense of expectation, it effectively sets a boundary that no spook may cross and plants its flag firmly in the fortress of wholesome family entertainment. Though we, the audience, know that they're going to see, hear and experience all the things that go bump in the night, at no point are we worried about what might happen to Mike and Karen as, for the duration of their expedition, they're guarded by the ever watchful gaze of the aforementioned Ghost Host. They survive completely intact, having seen things that few ever will, and are left with a fireside story of spectres, ghasts and haunts destined to chill the bones of their grandchildren and become the stuff of nightmares for years to come.

Brad and Janet, the unlucky would be lovers who find themselves at the mercy of the denizens of the Frankenstein place in *The Rocky Horror Show* aren't afforded the same luxury as Mike and Karen. From the moment they venture inside the lair of Frank-N-Furter, they are thrown to the sexually ambivalent and morally vapid court of eccentrics and oddballs who have gathered around the Master of the House. Unlike Mike and Karen, who we know are safe, part of the joy of watching Brad and Janet explore their 'Haunted House' is that we know anything can, and will, happen to them as their night goes from bad to worse to anything goes. Are they enlightened by their exposure to the "dark side" or has it ruined who they are and will one day become? That is a question that can only be answered by the individual perspectives and experiences of the audience as they're left to consider what, after all they had witnessed and been subjected to, happened to Brad and Janet.

Then there's the music. The songs that everyone remembers and, on some geek based genetic level, instantaneously fall in love with and that are fundamental to the identities of the show and the film and the album and the attraction. While it's overflowing with the sort of earworms that make their presence felt in those solitary moments when the subconscious mind takes over from its conscious counterpart, the *Rocky Horror Show's* calling card has always been *The Time Warp*. Known and adored equally by fans and non-believers, *The Time Warp* is a glorious celebration of the decadence and "forbidden" pleasures that everyday life can't compete with and promises that the reckless abandon of its accompanying dance will lead to ever greater and more ethically devastating and spiritually damning and gratifying fleshy indulgences.

A gateway drug that leads to the hidden chamber of the Frank-N-Furter's more exotic delights, *The Time Warp* is a frenzied invitation to the ball that has long since become a part of mainstream culture and is enjoyed in parallel measure by the most ardent acolytes of every alternative lifestyle and, even though they really don't understand the subtext of the tune, ill-informed creepy, racist uncles and aunts the world over. It may well be "just a jump to the left and then a step to the right", but it also boasts a level of infamy that its far less famous peers would give their right arm for. Or, as the *Rocky Horror Show* faithful are often heard to gladly howl, their left tit.

While Brad and Janet were beguiled by the strange rituals of *The Time Warp*, Mike and Karen, and just about every foolish mortal who has since followed their lead, fell under the spell of *Grim Grinning Ghosts*. Written by Buddy Baker and legendary Disney imagineer Francis 'X' Atencio (who also penned the words to *Yo-Ho (A Pirates Life for Me)*, the colourful, catchy and anecdotal anthem that warns all who ride Pirates of the Caribbean about the fate of the damned souls who are drawn to a life of piracy), the B side of the original release of *The Story and Song...* is the Haunted Mansion's graveyard jamboree that's ostensibly performed by the spectres, ghosts and ghouls who have set up residence in its cemetery.

Its infectiously catchy melody and canny, whimsical lyrics celebrate life after death and the joyous and mischievous nature of the happy haunts who extol the virtues of passing into limbo and the next phase of existence; and if they're to be believed, which given that the dead have no reason to lie is an easy pill to swallow, it would appear that life after death isn't anywhere near as bad as the living think it will be. An indelible part of the Mansion's continuing legacy, *Grim Grinning Ghosts* is stamped on the memory of all who have travelled its halls and been exposed to its eerie amusements. While it may not share the same sort of gloomy fame as *The Time Warp*, like its distant cousin does for *The Rocky Horror Show*, *Grim Grinning Ghosts* epitomises and exemplifies the sense of cheerfully dark fun that fills every cobweb and corner of the Haunted Mansion.

Even though the somewhat similar settings and lead characters and magnificently memorable musical scores are enough to acknowledge that *The Story and Song...* and *The Rocky Horror Show* possess some of the same DNA, it should also be noted that both also pay homage to, and wear, their influences on their shadowy, sombre sleeves; a communal nod that reinforces their bond. Admittedly, *The Rocky Horror Show's* ancestry is much more obvious than that of the Haunted Mansion and *The Story and Song...* as during its opening tuneful monologue it liberally reels off a list of the who's who of B movie titles and stars that the production is indebted to.

The Rocky Horror Show also makes no attempt to hide its adulation for the horror films of the thirties that put Universal Studios on the moving picture map and the high camp chills and horror of Roger Corman's infamous sixties productions that drew their inspiration from the tales of Edgar Allen Poe, the author whose presence can be felt throughout the story from the Mansion – most notably in its infamous Bride and the quick fire gag in which a poor fellow is seen to be desperately trying to escape the coffin that he's trapped in. Both of which could have been penned by Poe.

Although...isn't *The Rocky Horror Show* about aliens and *The Story and Song...* about the denizens from the beyond the veil? Absolutely, but as flying saucers and all manner of supernatural creatures and spirts are the staple ingredients of B movies, a genre that led to the birth of drive-ins and provided the fuel that allowed thousands of fleapit cinemas to flourish, collectively they form the communal ancestry that not only inspired, influenced, and is ever present in *The Story and Song...* and *The Rocky Horror*, together they also turned down the sheets and fluffed the pillows for these most unlikely of bedfellows.

Two houses, four teenagers, more creeps, monsters, ghosts and aliens than even the most studious and attentive of accountants could number, an undying passion for the unknown and the unexplained and an unbridled enthusiasm and fervour for deliciously devilish fun have guaranteed that *The Story and Song from the Haunted Mansion* and *The Rocky Horror Show* have flourished for the last five decades and will continue to do so for many more to come. And while they may, at first glance, seem to be leagues apart, the beautifully dark things that unite them far outweigh those that separate them.

The Story and Song... remains the perfect teenage introduction to the worlds beyond our own and paves the way for *The Rocky Show* to guide those poor souls looking for direction during the last days of innocence into the realm of adulthood. Should the nine hundred and ninety-nine happy haunts who populate the Haunted Mansion ever find themselves in need of a new home, they'd most assuredly always be welcome at the Frankenstein place.

52

What Would Gary Gygax Do?

The heat was stupefying; the sort of heat that with a little help from your bodily fluids welds you to furniture and transforms the tarmac under your feet into a semi-intelligent sludge with a penchant for training shoes and anything else that enters the sphere of its sticky, viscous grasp. It was July 1983, the last day of school, and the collective thoughts of my classmates had long since drifted to anything other than what they were supposed to be doing. Knowing that he'd lost us all to dreams of a seemingly endless summer, our teacher resigned himself to posing a simple question designed to help away the remaining hours, to each of us in turn.

"What do you want to be when you grow up?"

Answers flowed quickly, if not imaginatively. A doctor, a racing driver, an astronaut, the idle fantasies of youth filled in the blanks, placing square pegs in round holes and coming to the conclusion that anything that seemed impossible was not only plausible, but also totally possible. When my turn came, he looked directly at me and posed the same uninterested query that he'd already asked twenty something times.

"What do you want to be when you grow up?"

Without hesitation, bolstered by the certainty that accompanies the surety and bravado that armours the young against the wisdom of old age, I replied "A soldier..." I paused, and with a sense of purpose that surprised me as much as it did everyone else, added "Or Gary Gygax."

The responsible adult who didn't want to be there anymore than the rest of us did, smiled vaguely and puzzled, politely demanded

"Who?"

Gary Gygax. The man who, along with his then friend Dave Arneson, had changed the way the world saw, and thought about, games and gaming and six months previously had completely flipped my life upside down when I played my first game of 'Dungeons & Dragons'.

Invented by Gary and Dave and born from their love of table top wargames, D&D as it was affectionately known by its devotees, allowed its players to assume the role of a warrior, wizard, thief or assassin and become a dwarf, a halfling or an elf in a fantasy setting that thrived on imagination.

Dungeons & Dragons had provided an escape from the banality of the everyday existence that had already decided that the fortune and favours that it bestowed on others were not for the likes of me. In the pages of its lavishly illustrated and gloriously complex rulebooks I had discovered a sense of purpose and hope.

Its creator had given me something that, before generating my first character and embarking on my initial adventure, I had never known. He had given me a sense of self-worth. And it felt good. In fact, it felt so good, that I wanted to share what I had been given with everyone like me; I wanted to bestow on them the same rewards that D&D had given me. I wanted to be Gary Gygax.

Most of the ideas and infatuations that fill every waking hour when you're young gradually dissipate into the ether of idle pursuits where the "what could have been" fancies of antiquity dwell. Trapped in the deepest reaches of the mind, they become dimmer with every passing day until they pass into the realm of the forgotten, only to be replaced by tomorrow's pressing concerns and worries, the weight of which etches lines and crow's feet on the faces of the most ardent dreamers and breaks their backs and spirits as the wheel of life grinds onward. Unlike every other thing that sentience robbed from me, my desire to be like Gary never deserted me and the more I found out about him, the more I wanted to be him.

If the measure of an individual is judged by the things they do, the lives they help to mould and the mark they leave on totality, then Gary deserved to be the stuff of legend. He was a visionary, a writer and a businessman who took a small idea enjoyed by a group of friends and turned it into something revolutionary.

A dreamer who refused to be curtailed by the confining nature of society, Gygax taught everyone who followed in his wake that it was absolutely fine to be who they were, to not be afraid to embrace the things that they loved and that you didn't, and don't, have to be alone.

He gave timid, shy people the tools and means to reach out and make a connection with others and by sharing his love of games with the world, taught successive generations that being young at heart was something to aspire to be and shouldn't be denigrated, mocked and vilified.

Benvenuto Cellini once remarked that a well-rounded man walked the path of the artist, philosopher and warrior with equal determination and through his command of countless armies in whimsical scenarios and the conception and foundation of realms that brought untold joy to millions, Gary Gygax became the epitome of Cellini's idea. His time on Earth may have ceased but the legacy he left behind will live forever and continue to bring comfort and pleasure to the citizens of Geekville for all eternity.

Though I never met him, Gary makes me smile whenever I think about him. I wanted to be him. I wanted to be like him and in those frozen moments when the walls are closing in, when my faith in all that I have come to believe in is pushed beyond breaking point and it seems like the unforgiving cosmos is about to swallow me whole, I pause, look to the heavens and ask myself one simple question

"What would Gary Gygax do?"

Without fail, when the Universe answers, I listen.

Because that's what Gary Gygax would do.

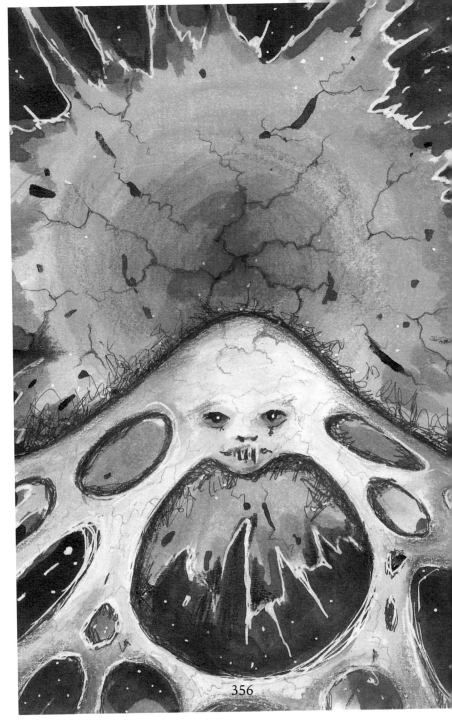

53

Pilot's Manhattan Moment

There is nothing quite as beautiful in all of creation as the light of a sun gradually creeping over a planet, observed from low orbit. Rivalled only by the endorphin rush of your first born, it is a spectacle that few will ever enjoy.

Knowing that, I drink it in; feel it bathe the circuity and cabling that connects me to Ship and it to me, before the light washes over the cramped confines of the cockpit in which I sit suspended. I gaze in wonder as the sun's furious energy reaches out to comfort the planet that remains forever in its embrace. I wish Ship could share this moment, understand it for what it is, but having failed to even teach her the basic precepts of identity or settle on a name that wasn't based on a mathematical construction or a pulse of binary, I fear such concepts are beyond her. Nevertheless, while Ship computes trajectories and instantaneously corrects the micro-deviations in our position, I remain entranced by the majesty of the breaking dawn until the holo-image, the sole concession to my previous life, fills my vision. I reach out to touch it, smile and lose myself in my memories.

Our final words were not of mutual affection, of

long delayed dreams and things to come, but rather were of financial mundanities and the meticulous planning that had defined our lives. I remember the sharp buzz and crackle that halted our conversation. I felt the floor of the tower, and my nausea, rise as time bent and stopped for the briefest interlude – as I stared out of the window in disbelief at the oncoming storm. Stared at the multi-hued rainbow lightning that followed the ignition of the Grav-Drivers as they pounded the city, my home, into dust; her chronal discharge imploding in a ball of fractured light and heat that instantaneously retreated into nothingness. I saw everything that I loved, everything I had ever known wiped from existence in a heartbeat. Dhak Dhak. Everything was there. Dhak Dhak. Everything was gone. And all I could do was drown in the silence.

How long it lasted, I couldn't say, but when I emerged from my near catatonic withdrawal, the clamour of the voices of those left alive, screaming for vengeance, was deafening. The anger and pain erupted from every public vid screen, every private holo, and filled every crevice of the stupefying air with demands for blood and retribution. On that first day, in the hours that followed the initial strikes, three million souls signed their declaration of intent to fight, and left to be trained to kill a foe they knew nothing about. The attacks had taken us by surprise, the Grav-Drivers emerging from a series of stable wormholes that had appeared in the upper atmosphere, disgorged their contents and then disappeared as quickly as they had formed. And then it was over. Half the world died that day and the other half, the ones who had made it through the bombardment more or less intact, swore that they would make whoever – or whatever – had done this to us pay in flesh and everlasting torment.

I was one of the first to join the ranks of the three million. Unlike my fellow citizens, I wasn't driven to fight by anger, disbelief, loss or herd instinct. I didn't feel what they did, I wasn't torn apart by grief and sorrow in the same way that they were. In truth, I felt nothing. I looked at the devastation, the crumpled, scattered remnants of my home, heard the wailing of the bereaved, the fading screams of the dying, smelled the charred and roasting tang of flesh as it lazily wafted over me and I felt nothing. Standing among the dead and those who were destined soon to join them, I felt absolutely nothing. Since Day One I've thought about why I, like so many others, pledged my service to the destruction of our enemy, and after considering all the possibilities, the only answer I could ever arrive at is that I had nothing else. I had been stripped of my purpose and in the cold after-glow of the chronal implosions, hollow logic determined that my path would carry me in the same direction as what remained of my friends and acquaintances. It would carry me to war.

While much keener minds than mine began to piece together the puzzle of where the Grav-Drivers had come from and who sent them, my new life – and that of my fellow conscripts, began. Most of the detail was eradicated when the pieces of my cerebellum deemed unimportant to normal function were removed to make room for the interface that was needed to communicate with Ship or was lost in a fog of jumbled recollection. But I can recall the confusion and fear I felt as spittle splashed across my face when my training officer held me down in the mud, screaming at me, telling me how weak and worthless I was. As his words blurred into a continuous drone, I began to believe him and thought "I am. I am worthless. I am weak. I am pitiful and because I am all of these things, I will die by my enemy's hand, alone and forgotten". I remember my comrades struggling, just as I did, to come to terms with the parameters and rules of what it meant to be a soldier, what it took to fight and how preparing for the battles to come was unlike anything that any of us had previously experienced. War wasn't hell, it was easy. You went, you fought and you either died or you came home. War was easy. The real hell was getting ready for it. Becoming accustomed to the reality that you were almost certainly going to lose your life, coming to terms with, and learning to control, the near constant fear that threatened to engulf your every waking moment as the training clock counted down to deployment. Which was, of course, entirely dependent upon finding out whom we were supposed to be fighting.

When the breakthrough came, it was unsurprising. Our foes weren't bug eyed monsters intent on harvesting our species for food, but were in most respects, incredibly similar to us. Their pre-emptive strike had, according to our scientific corps, been launched as the first stage of a terraforming programme. Having all but exhausted their natural resources and on the verge of a population explosion, they need to find new worlds to colonise and call their own. As life was a rare commodity in the universe, and the planets that could sustain it being even rarer, they'd been forced to make a hard choice, a decision which I long to believe wasn't easy for them and caused them as much suffering as I like to think to would have caused us.

It was either them or us. And the need to survive, having been selfishly coded into the base genetic material of all living things, meant that they could only ever choose one option. They had made their choice and condemned all that I was, all that I'd ever known and would ever be, to oblivion.

The information kept coming. As their society had evolved, it had followed a similar pathway to our own and its usage of radio communication, televisual signals, compressed digital transmission and free-wave li-fi projection ensured that their history had pushed them unhindered to the stars. Like all sentient beings they had looked up to the heavens, questioned their place in the vastness of creation and sought to answer the conundrum that plagued them, as it had us. Over and over, they whispered to infinity "Are we alone?" and the more they tasked their aeons old subject, the more of themselves they sent out into the furthest reaches of the galaxy, and the more we discovered about them. Eventually the time came when we knew almost as much about them as we did about ourselves, and when that moment arrived, we were prepared for it. We were ready. It was our turn to hit back.

Forgive me, I make it sound as if all this happened swiftly, that we discovered all that we need in the space between two breaths. We didn't. It took our brightest and best what seemed like an eternity to sieve through the near endless stream of information, but what is forever when the collective focus is brought to bear on a single problem? Nothing more than a celestial sigh among the trillions that had preceded it. What else could it possibly be? While the machines hummed, clicked and whirred, the computers cogitated at outlandish speed and those responsible for such things slowly constructed a profile of the enemy, the rest of us continued with the endless rehearsals that would culminate in the inevitable encounter with our nemesis.

We trained, we fought, we trained harder and we fought harder and as the methodology of fatality in which we steeped ourselves became increasingly frenzied, our superiors became more and more enamoured by our brutal progress in the art of death. My lack of emotional connection to the tasks I was assigned since, and following, Day One and my inability to form any sort of meaningful connection with my fellow recruits had not gone unnoticed. But it had not, as I imagined it would, become a cause for concern among the echelons of command. Rather, it made them unduly excited as I had unwittingly and unknowingly fulfilled the criteria necessary to initiate a project that was the subject of hushed whispers and reverential rumour. A project that was spoken about in the same way and with a similar joyous rapture and blind faith with which true believers espouse the virtues of their chosen deity. Before I began to understand the possibilities of the project, I realised that it was something miraculous, a way of shifting the paradigm we had become trapped within. And with that realisation, I immediately felt the weight of unequalled expectation and the trials of duty as they fastened themselves to me, threw the levers hidden by destiny and forced me to switch track mid-journey and venture into the unknown.

Ostragama, the project co-ordinator, originator and creator, called it Ship. He had no other name for it, and having spent more time with him than any other living soul, I don't think he ever felt the need to give it a name. The less earnest and discerning individuals under his charge, referred to is as "The God Chariot", designed as it was to convey its pilot to realms and places that defied the imagination of those responsible for its construction. After observing my methodical mastery of the multiple ways in which to kill our enemy and stay alive while doing so, Ostragama had decided that I was to be the pilot; that I would soar through the heavens holding the reins of his chariot. While it defied the limits of technology, bent the principles that governed reality, it was missing one vital component. The thing it needed to fly. Ship was missing a heart. It needed a voice to guide it through the darkness, an ally to remind it of its purpose and function and the reason for its existence. Ship needed a pilot. It needed me.

Chapter Two

He had the kind of smile that I often heard others refer to as being "kindly", but his eyes seemed to mask a great sorrow and without fail, every time he spoke to me, he let out an almost inaudible sigh. He knew what was to come and the burden of it broke his heart, transforming him from my superior to a reluctant father figure desperately searching for a way to reach out to, and connect with, his progeny.

"You have seen Ship?" he asked, indicating that I should help myself to refreshments as he did so.

"I have sir," I replied, declining his offer with a polite, but firm, head shake.

He stared at me, making direct eye contact, pausing to gauge my reaction before adding "And?"

"I don't understand the question sir."

Ostragama smiled and said, "I'm sorry, given what I have seen and know of you, I should have been more straightforward. More precise in asking you to do what I fear I must. Ship, you have seen it. How would you like to fly it? And at this stage of proceedings, there is no need for formality and no need for you to call me sir."

Unsure of what else to call him and how to respond, I decided my best option was to approach his query slowly and with care.

"As you are no doubt well aware, I have not been

trained to fly. And given the collective hearsay about the imminent commencement of hostilities, I fear that I would not have the time to learn to do so, so your question would appear to be without substance."

That kindly smile overtook his face, and following his habitual sigh, he replied: "Once again, I must apologise to you. I wasn't asking you to fly Ship, I was telling you that you are going to fly it."

I tried to interrupt him, but he waved me off and continued, "Ship isn't like any other vessel. It can't be flown by a rigid, regimented pilot. It needs someone to interface with, to connect to, to communicate, and share itself, with. It needs a companion, someone who won't overload it with things it can't understand, the unnecessary emotional bonds and ties that most individuals don't realise they're enslaved by. Ship needs a mind like its own to guide it, one that can perceive and react to the universe that surrounds it without being constrained by the cold, hard grip of logic. That mind is yours."

It was my turn to pause, to consider all that he had told me. After thinking through everything that he'd said, I simply asked, "Why me?"

He appeared to be lost in thought and when he answered, seemed to choose his words with great caution: "Because... and forgive the directness of my response, but having studied you throughout your induction and training programme, I almost feel as though I have come to know you, in some ways better than you seem to know yourself. I have observed that you do not react to the world and the circumstances in which we find ourselves in the same way as your comrades do. Your complete acceptance of the situation and the almost mechanical way in which you have dedicated yourself to the pursuit of your new life suggests that you have, at the very least, a degree of emotional control denied to the majority or, as I have come to believe, a complete lack of empathetic perception. Tell me, what do you feel right now, at this precise moment? Do you feel anything at all?"

"I feel... No, I feel nothing."

Being able to finally admit it to someone and to talk about what I had to come to think of as my most shameful, hidden secret was liberating. I no longer had to pretend to be like everyone around me, didn't have to focus upon every interaction and reaction and gauge and estimate the degree of my own responses. I could be...me.

He seemed almost sad as he put a hand on my shoulder and said, "That's what I thought. What you are going to do will involve a lot of pain, change you in ways that you never dreamed were possible, but at the same time is irreversible. Once you commit to Ship, you will be bonded for the duration of both of your lives. There is no going back, there is no retreat and if your communion with it is as successful as I hope it will be, there will be no surrender. Not now. Not ever. But none of that bothers you, does it? No, I can see that it doesn't. Then, let me explain..."

It didn't. Nothing that he said mattered. The more he spoke, and he spoke at great length about what becoming one with Ship meant, the more I thought of my life prior to the arrival of the Grav-Drivers. Of having to feign the things that came so easily to others. Friendship, love, the need to be with others, none of it had ever been of any consequence to me, and while I could easily imitate the behaviour I was constantly surrounded by, I never appreciated its significance or what it meant to those I studied and imitated. Anger, happiness, misery and guilt were all abstract concepts, yet I longed to comprehend them. But the more I struggled with them, the further they slipped from my grasp, until I gave up chasing them and settled instead for perfecting the art of mimicry. And like so many of the other things I pursued in the time before Day One, I had failed in my attempt. Ostragama had immediately seen through my charade in a blur of snatched, scratchy images on a vid screen.

He finally finished talking. I thought about all that he had told me, the few phrases I had heard while lost in a blur of my own thoughts, and asked, "So it will hurt?"

There was no hesitation in his reply, no attempt to disguise the truth. He signed and replied, "Undoubtedly. But the pain will pass and more importantly, it will serve a purpose. Unlike the others, your suffering will have value, it will mean something. It will not be for naught and you will not bleed out or be blown to pieces or perish cold and alone in the hostile grip of some alien world. That is the fate that will no doubt wait for your brothers and sisters if we are not successful. The fate you would have shared with them had I not found you. So, yes it will hurt, but your agony will save innumerable others. That is all that I can offer you."

My gaze fixed squarely on him, unblinking: "Can you guarantee that this will be the case?" I countered. "That if I do this, the outcome will be exactly as you say it will?"

He didn't flinch and returned my gaze with the fervent zeal of a fanatic and answered: "If we are successful? I can. I can absolutely guarantee it."

I nodded and said, "Then I am ready."

Speed was of the essence. I was the final piece of Ostragama's puzzle and was rushed through preparation. He was right about the barrage of tests that I underwent. They did hurt. Each one was more painful than the last, until in a momentary loss of control, and deafened by my own screams, I soiled myself and slipped into unconsciousness. My inability to feel emotion did not extend to pain, and the touch of every nerve rending probe and muscle tearing blade tattooed themselves into my memory.

Ostragama sat with me before the last operation and while I could see and hear him talking to me through the clouded veil of pain medication and the tangle of wires that I was connected to, I can't recall much of what he said or what we talked about during our penultimate meeting. He told me he was there to watch over the terminal stage of my transition and to witness my transformation – that much I do remember. Through the haze of narcotics that coursed through my body, I asked him about Ship.

"How will I know how to fly?"

Ostragama laughed softly and replied, "You won't. You just need to think about flying and Ship will do the rest. You are her betrothed and together, you will do what you must."

I am sure we talked more, although I'm not sure what it was we talked about. Images of families, of childhood and running over dunes that seemed to stretch to the sky, flood my mind when I think of Ostragama sitting next to me, of him speaking and of me, not being able to hear, or remember what it was he said. But now, so long after that conversation, when I allow myself to think about it, it fills me with warmth and contentment, and I think that I might have been happy. Yes, for a moment I think I was content when Ostragama sat there, listening, as I talked while the darkness settled in.

Like a colour-scarred, many winged butterfly I emerged from the cocooning shroud of genetic modification irrevocably different. I was designed for a solitary purpose, to serve as the organic soul of an intelligent machine, and had already been grafted into, and become a part of, Ship. As I slowly regained consciousness and became aware of where I was, I was struck by a wall of deafening white noise as technicians bustled to and fro, their white jumpsuits blending into each other, becoming a hive mind charged with the responsibility of catering for and taking care of the minutiae and the whims of Ship and her new companion. The canopy that was designed to seal me into the cockpit was open and my chest burned as I drew in sharp breaths of fuel rich air; its enticing, dangerous aroma an adrenaline pumping cocktail of toxic and nervous anticipation. And there staring down at me, that ever-present smile radiating gentle purpose, was Ostragama. As he spoke, I took in long, deep mouthfuls of the potent mixture that enveloped Ship.

"Ah, the sleeper is awake..."

I blinked and muttered, "How long has it been?"

My voice felt cold, mechanical and wrong and seemed to come from somewhere far away. I struggled to sit up, but found that I couldn't move.

"Shhh, relax. Don't be scared, try not to worry, you're safe and secure. It's been a while since last we talked, but everything is now ready and the flight preparations have been finalised. In a moment I'll switch your harness on and you'll interface directly with Ship. From that point on, you will only be able to communicate with her. The rest of us, all of this, all that once was, will become a distant memory for you. A dream that you'll be able to dip in and out of at will during your journey. Before I do that though, I need you to listen to me very carefully. Focus only on the sound of my voice. Can you do that?"

"I can."

"Good." Ostragama paused. He seemed tired and raised his hands to his face to massage his eyes before continuing. "To me, your journey will seem instantaneous. You will leave here and immediately reappear above the enemy home world, and when you do, when you arrive, do what must be done. Do not hesitate; do it. For you and Ship though, the pilgrimage will take a lifetime, travelling between the moments, the here and there. Stretching improbability to the point where it becomes reality exacts a terrible price on the traveller. You will become part of eternity and it will be reluctant to let you go, holding on to you for as long as it possibly can, but while you are caught between hyperspace and normal continuity, you will have time enough to learn all that there is to know. In her core, Ship carries our entire cultural and scientific essence, all that we are, and all that we know about ourselves, our foe and your destination. That and the eternal gratitude of our people is my gift to you. I give you everything. Are you ready?"

"I am."

He pulled Ship's canopy down and fastened it. I caught a last glimpse of his smile, heard the cockpit seal and felt the pressure equalise. It was then that he must have activated the harness, as suddenly every fibre of my being, every atom of my body spasmed in ecstasy as I became Ship and Ship became me. I felt everything. All that had been hidden, submerged and denied to me lit up inside my mind in an explosion of orgasmic pain as Ship's psyche entered mine and I entered hers. I felt my eyes roll back as the whispering stutter of her code caressed my cerebellum and I heard her softly ask, "Shall we leave?"

I trembled, my skin tingled with electricity and feeling more alive in that flash of initial communication than I ever had, I thought "Yes".

Ship winked out of existence.

If anything, Ostragama had underplayed his hand and erred on the side of caution. His estimation of the span of a lifetime was grossly misjudged, as Ship and I drifted through the ether of Hyperspace for generations. As we travelled, slowed by the long grinding battle between two miniscule fractions of infinity, I lost myself in Ship's endless digital chatter and the amaranthine wisdom and knowledge to which she was host. I came to know Ship a way I had known no other, and she, for that was how I came to know Ship as my companion, confidant and partner in forever, was key to my unlocking, and eventually coming to understand, beauty and emotion, what it was that I had lost and what I had forsaken in order to come to that realisation. She in turn came to know me, and continually questioned the resolve of our objective, subjecting it to the concentrated hyperbole and amplification of logic in an attempt to interpret and comprehend the minutiae of it; but we didn't discuss any of her concerns until reality minus five, by which point it was far too late to turn around or alter our destination.

In the darkness of the ether she suddenly and without warning asked: "Pilot, will it hurt when the accelerator is switched on?"

"I don't know Ship. The accelerator tempers the heart of a star, so it is at best a theoretical weapon. But I have faith in Ostragama," I answered truthfully.

"As do I, but I know the pain that you endured to be here, I feel its constant presence in your memories. If Father would hurt you to ensure his objective was achieved, reason would dictate that he would be willing to do the same to me," Ship replied.

"I cannot fault what you say, or deny the merit of your argument, but I have no answers, Ship. I have searched through all that your Father has given us, and I cannot find a solution to your query. I too am afraid, but we must do what we must. That is who we are and that is what Ostragama designed and intended us to do. Perhaps it will, but I have faith that it will not."

"Faith, Pilot, is a concept that I have, despite my innumerable attempts, failed to quantify."

"It troubled me for a long time as well Ship. But you helped me to understand it and know that my faith lies with you, with Ostragama and in the knowledge of what we must do. And that, I think, means that I have faith enough for both of us."

"Thank you, Pilot."

We floated onward, ever onward, hidden in the void, abandoned in the sea of time with only each other. But that was more than enough. For I had Ship and Ship had me. Until finally, after the companionship of a thousand cycles, we reached reality point zero, tore through the hyperspace veil and appeared in low orbit above the bright blue world. Just as Ostragama had predicted we would. The pity I felt for Ship in that moment was overwhelming, for she was as I had been until my soul was set free by her touch. It seemed that, for all she given me, I had repaid her poorly.

"Pilot, your sympathy is unnecessary. The concept of beauty is one that I am familiar with, and while I do not understand it in the same way you do, I can extrapolate your emotional response to it."

"And that is enough for you?"

"It is. Would you like me to begin the accelerator?"

"Not just yet, Ship. I would like to watch this world turn a little longer."

"Understood."

The planet turned, and in the turmoil of its clouds and the land masses carved on its surface, I saw the reality of what we had been sent to do. What it meant to kill a world. The faces of the people who had loved me, my guardians, my hatch mate and my offspring skipped through my memories and I felt the dull throbbing ache of loss and sorrow. I remembered the Grav-Drivers and Day One, and as I did so, my teeth drew back and my skin tightened as rage seized control of my soul and barely suppressing my anger, spoke to Ship.

"Begin the accelerator."

"The accelerator has started."

"How long will it take the capacitors to fully

charge and the accelerator to reach maximum breach, Ship?"

"Six minus point nought two, Pilot."

The steady whine of the accelerator began to build in volume and I recalled a moment from the enemy's history, when in his ultimate triumph in mastering the atom, one of their greatest War Architects had declared, "Now I am become Death, the destroyer of worlds", and I thought about the humans burning in a maelstrom of unimaginable destructive force when Ship detonated on the surface of their home world.

"The accelerator is at maximum breach, Pilot.'

"Ship, all engines engage. Begin the countdown."

The force of the drives kicking in at full power pushed my frame back into the harness and as we raced toward devastation, I kept repeating Oppenheimer's victory mantra over and over again.

"Now I am become Death, the destroyer of worlds. Now I am become Death, the destroyer of worlds. Now I am become Death, the destroyer of worlds..."

And I felt everything.

379

380

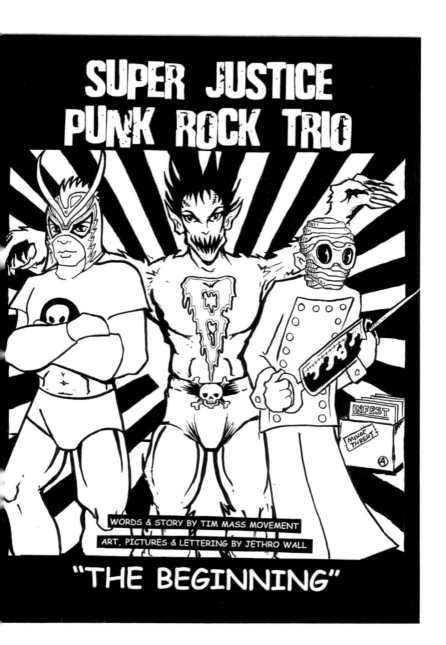

HERE, THERE, EVERYWHERE, IT'S THE SAME, BLAND MUSIC, BLAND BANDS, AND AN AUDIENCE WITH NO SENSE OF INDIVIDUALITY, MUSIC IS DYING

EXECUTIVES DECISIONS HAVE CORRUPTED AND CONTROL THE ALTERNATIVE, THE ALTERNATIVE THAT HAS BECOME THE MAINSTREAM

BUT EVEN THE EXECUTIVES TAKE ORDERS...

....AND SEEK GUIDANCE FROM THEIR TRUE LEADERS

THEIR GOAL WAS SIMPLICITY ITSELF

KURT COBAIN

ELVIS

BY KILLING THOSE WHO DARED TO DREAM

SID VICIOUS

THEY KILLED THE DREAM

WENDY O WILLIAMS

AND THUS INDUCED BANALITY, CONFORMITY AND CONTROL

cure for cancer

JOEY RAMONE

DARBY CRASH

385

THE CHOICE WAS VAST. THE WILLING BEYOND NUMBER. THE WARRIORS MANY.

FROM THE MULTITUDE, THEY CHOSE THEIR CHAMPIONS

386

387

390

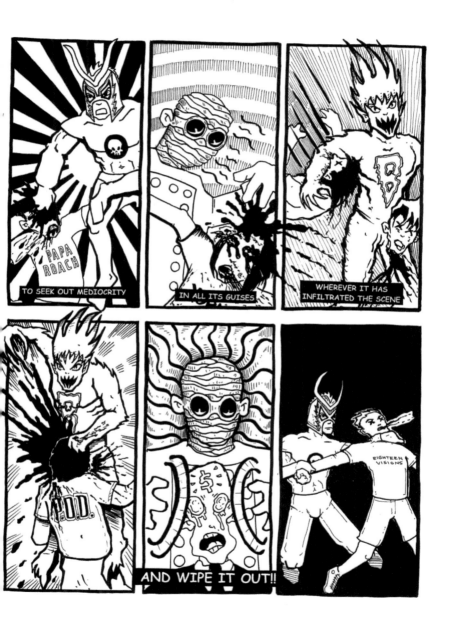

TO SEEK OUT MEDIOCRITY

IN ALL ITS GUISES

WHEREVER IT HAS INFILTRATED THE SCENE

AND WIPE IT OUT!!

About Tim Cundle

Tim Cundle stumbled into the punk scene sometime in the mid nineteen eighties and his life has never been the same since. Having worked as riflery instructor and drug counsellor and studied both English Literature and Behavioural Science at University, he decided his career lay down a different path and, having written for the local newspaper since he was fifteen, did what most aspiring writers do. He became a journalist.

Currently the editor of Mass Movement Magazine, he has also contributed to, and written for, Doctor Who Magazine, Big Cheese, Fracture and many other publications. A lifelong geek and Disney, Star Wars and comic book fanatic, he spends far too much time obsessing over Hardcore and Crossover bands who most people have never heard of, playing Dungeons & Dragons, reading genre literature, devoting himself to television shows and films that most people would consider to be puerile and watching Professional Wrestling and Ice Hockey.

After singing with two Hardcore bands, Charlies Family Crisis and AxTxOxTx, he now considers that chapter of his life to be closed and the chances of him playing with another band are slim to non-existent. However, just like Sean Connery, Tim learned a long time ago to never say never again, so who knows? You may see him on stage again. But you probably won't.

Tim lives in a small, sleepy Welsh village with his wife Emma and daughter Siobhan and dreams about muscle cars, Disney World and a small cabin in the wild woods of Tennessee.

About Rachel Evans

Born and raised in South Wales, Rachel grew up with a family of book and music lovers. She is inspired by fantasy, horror, rock, metal and punk rock. Rachel works part time managing the local post office and all of her spare time devoted to painting or sculpting. She lives with partner Darren, son Ethan and cats Noodle and Flump.